£4.99

CW00407189

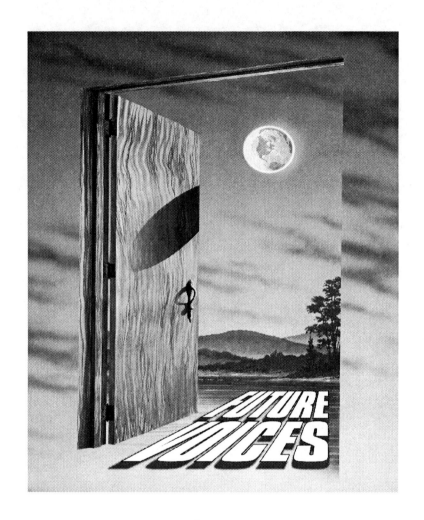

# FROM SOMERSET

Edited by Emma Marsden

First published in Great Britain in 2000 by
*YOUNG WRITERS*
Remus House,
Coltsfoot Drive,
Woodston,
Peterborough, PE2 9JX
Telephone (01733) 890066

HB ISBN 0 75431 761 7
SB ISBN 0 75431 762 5

# FOREWORD

This year, the Young Writers' Future Voices competition proudly presents a showcase of the best poetic talent from over 42,000 up-and-coming writers nationwide.

Successful in continuing our aim of promoting writing and creativity in children, our regional anthologies give a vivid insight into the thoughts, emotions and experiences of today's younger generation, displaying their inventive writing in its originality.

The thought, effort, imagination and hard work put into each poem impressed us all and again the task of editing proved challenging due to the quality of entries received, but was nevertheless enjoyable. We hope you are as pleased as we are with the final selection and that you continue to enjoy *Future Voices From Somerset* for many years to come.

# CONTENTS

## King Edward's School

| | |
|---|---|
| Simon Lynn | 48 |
| Edward Randle | 48 |
| Sam Sheppard | 49 |
| Henry Williamson | 49 |
| Neil Campbell | 50 |
| James Burrell | 50 |
| Nicholas Connolly | 51 |
| Jessica Ost | 52 |
| Craig Borland | 52 |
| William Jones | 53 |
| Tom Jones | 53 |
| Kate Clark | 54 |
| Lewis Topley | 54 |
| Ella Morison | 55 |
| Louise Fisher | 56 |
| Gavin Leesam | 56 |
| Eleanor-Louise Kenning | 57 |
| David Hoare | 57 |
| Madeline Coleborn | 58 |
| Anna Brownrigg | 59 |
| Sam Dawson | 60 |
| John McBride | 60 |
| Andrew White | 61 |
| Tim Wagstaff | 62 |
| Tom Hamilton | 62 |
| George Glen | 63 |
| Charles Barter | 64 |
| Louise Knight | 64 |
| Katharine Pooley | 65 |
| Matthew Tupper | 66 |
| Edward Hollis | 67 |

## Kings of Wessex School

| | |
|---|---|
| Emma Cullen | 68 |
| Oliver Morris | 69 |
| Joe Woodburn | 70 |
| Jennifer Wainwright | 71 |

Norton Hill School

| | |
|---|---:|
| Jessica Simpson | 71 |
| Aileen Bachrach | 72 |
| Brad Whittock | 73 |
| Sarah Macey | 74 |
| Daniel Lambert | 74 |
| Adele Wright | 75 |
| Samantha Newman | 76 |
| Becky Pearce | 76 |
| Penelope Roberts | 77 |
| Jonathon Hoare | 77 |
| Gary Harvey | 78 |
| Frankie Bray | 78 |
| Abigail Bawden | 79 |
| Danielle Brooks | 80 |
| Katie Fishlock | 81 |
| Michael Hayhoe | 81 |
| Stephanie Postbechild | 82 |
| Kathryn Angwin | 82 |
| Natalie Kenrick | 83 |
| Charlotte Hunter | 84 |
| Amy Atkins | 85 |
| Lee Marks | 85 |
| Alex Brain | 86 |
| Hayley Cribb | 86 |
| Jennifer Tapper | 87 |
| Dan Redgewell | 88 |
| Kate Lawrence | 89 |
| Aaron Welch | 89 |
| Jacob Ingram | 90 |
| Jessica Colbourne | 91 |
| Hannah Yeates | 92 |
| Ben Parker | 93 |
| Felicity Vine | 94 |
| Helen Warne | 95 |
| Melanie Brent | 96 |
| Richard Curtis | 96 |
| Emma Dall | 97 |

| | |
|---|---|
| Lisa Wheeler | 97 |
| Becca Clarke | 98 |
| Luke Collins | 98 |
| Matthew Harle | 99 |
| Frances Mullins | 99 |
| Melissa Kendall | 100 |
| Ben Chard | 101 |
| Alan Miles | 102 |
| Adam Martin | 102 |
| Kayleigh Lewis | 103 |
| Michaela Beale | 103 |
| James Clark | 104 |
| Jade Corp | 104 |
| Peri Harris | 105 |
| Louise Hole | 106 |
| Russell Gould | 106 |
| Daniel Rogers | 107 |
| Michelle Bohan | 108 |
| Sophie Louise McCarthy | 109 |
| Cally Lane | 110 |
| Lauren Trippick | 111 |
| Alex Price | 111 |
| Kirsty Diclaudio | 112 |
| James Bona | 112 |
| Alison Gillard | 113 |
| Sam Pratten | 113 |
| Hannah Jones | 114 |
| Jemma Taylor | 115 |
| Todd Lane | 116 |
| Andrew Withers | 116 |
| Tom Williams | 117 |
| Laura Smith | 117 |
| Jen Welfare | 118 |

Oldfield School

| | |
|---|---|
| Harriet Gordon | 118 |
| Leanne Burgess | 119 |
| Alice Palfrey | 119 |

St Mary's School, Calne

*The Poems*

# WHY . . .?

Why is there sorrow and sadness?
Why is there war and hate?
Why is there poverty and selfishness?
Why is it always too late?
Why is there terror and hurt?
Why is there destruction and death?

Why isn't there more joy and happiness?
Why isn't there peace or any cure?
Why isn't there more love and friendship?
Why can't they live for today?
Why isn't there more sharing and caring?
Why can't it happen today?

There's not enough help for the living
Is it too late to change now?

*Jess Wills  (12)*
*Chilton Trinity School*


# HATE

Hate storms about in jagged black and red clothes,
Breaking people, all life he loathes,
Slicing with his spiky sword,
Throwing bolts of lightning, starting
     wars because he's bored,
His terrible green eyes burn into your soul,
Burning bright like lumps of coal,
Growling low threats in his deep scratchy voice,
Being hateful is his choice . . .

*Matthew J Underwood*
*Chilton Trinity School*

## THE FAIR

Walking towards the fair in excitement,
Being able to hear music banging
And beating like drums
Taking a daily sniff of candyfloss,
                    toffee apples and hot dogs
Zooming straight to your nose.
Generators pumping and rattling like snakes,
In the desert.
Walking closer and closer,
Lights flashing, making different patterns
                    and bright colours
Making a gleam over the night sky.
Inside the fair pick a dart,
Straight in the bull's-eye!
Prize given -
A little red bulldog.
Top Buzz flying high in the sky,
Spinning, twisting and tossing in every direction.
Chaos swaying up and down,
Giving you a G-force and turning your belly over
Like going over a humpback bridge,
Eggs in space
Turning and whizzing around,
Whoosh, on your way down.
Time to leave.
Walking back through West Street
'25p each or 5 for a pound.'
Candyfloss swirling and whirling around
Crossing the road
Looking over your shoulder
Being able to see the gleam
Above the fair in the night sky.

*Dean Taylor  (14)*
*Chilton Trinity School*

## THE FAIR

The sounds of fear yelling, screaming.
The colour of the flashing lights like lightning.
The sugary sweet smell of fresh doughnuts.
The loud ride music banging and clashing together.
The revolting smell of petrol like a gas station.
The taste of sweet candyfloss melting in your mouth.
The loud shrieks of excitement.
The smell of the cigarette smoke everywhere.
The smell of freshly-cooked burgers drifting in the air.
The sight of fear when going on a high ride.
The rattling of money falling out of people's pockets.
The cold shiny metal of rides like robots.
The sound of people shouting from the market stalls.
The fierce pushing of the crowds in West Street.
All the different senses from the fair, all at the same time.

*Tanya Hughes  (14)*
*Chilton Trinity School*


## THE MOON IS . . .

The moon is a silver coin,
Eaten into every day, returning every night.

The moon is a silent night-glow,
Down a dark and gloomy alleyway.

The moon is a round silver eye,
Peering down upon the world.

The moon is the top of a metal bin,
Wheeled in every morning, wheeled out
                        every evening.

*Zowie Brooker  (12)*
*Chilton Trinity School*

## I HOPE . . .

I hope . . .
That people will live in peace,
Peace that is everlasting,
Everlasting like the world.

I hope . . .
That there will be no poor people in the world,
World without poverty
Poverty that is ruining people's lives.

I hope . . .
That future generations of children will live a good life,
Life without war and crime,
Crime that is present today.

I hope . . .
That people will look after our Earth.
Earth that keeps us alive,
Alive, well and healthy.

I hope . . .
That people won't pollute the air,
Air that is very important to everyone,
Everyone on this Earth.

I hope . . .
That people enjoy their world,
World of peace and joy,
Joy that everyone shares.

*Keri Dunderdale  (13)*
*Chilton Trinity School*

# X

For that heartbreaking time
The sky closed in
and the Earth closed in.

I found myself cocooned and confounded
to friends, thoughts and feelings.

       Everything that seems to matter.

As time moved on,
And, as I moved on
I began to realise
That this was a growth in maturity

Like a caterpillar to a butterfly
I moved into a new aspect of my life

In that as a caterpillar is simplified
to a case of surrounding,
I break from body,
to thoughts, feelings and questions

And from this cocooned mess
a matured caterpillar absconds

And as the caterpillar has developed wings
I have a new understanding
And like the butterfly,
       a growth of beautiful maturity.

*Jonathan Lee  (15)*
*Chilton Trinity School*

# THE ISLAND

The calling wind draws my attention,
Across the horizon as an island drifts,
Waves crashing,
Rolling and screaming,
Falling in the ocean,
Deeper than ever.
As I draw closer,
I am pulled by a force,
My eyes attached to a castle,
Coasting off-course.
I'm near, it's still calling,
Still rolling.
Great as could be,
Tall and tumbling,
Falling down.
Now that I'm here,
The calling has stopped,
Alone like a floating yacht.

*Katy Bone (12)*
*Chilton Trinity School*


# WAR AND PEACE

A field of greed,
Bullets pour like hailstones,
Blood spreads like rivers,
Soldiers' eyes filled with fear,
Their hands shaking.
They pray for forgiveness for what they are
about to do,
Their conscience raised to their side,
They aim, guilt spreads and a life is taken.

I only wish that guns were flowers,
That bullets were petals,
That danced in a light breeze
As the shimmering rays of sun surrounded
the bright flowers.
I only wish that greed was non-existent,
That generosity had no limits.
But then again I only wish.

*Jess Bowerman  (12)*
*Chilton Trinity School*

## ZOOM LENS

Standing on a cliff
Two dots out ahead
Nearer and nearer the shape
Starts to form.
Two boats colourful and bright
Closer still I see a rope.
Bigger and bolder the picture
Soon takes place
A figure moving pulling on a rope
Softly swaying, the boat rocks
Moving in I see a hand
Waving at the passers-by.
The boat is big and swaying
Softly.
Closer still I see a rod,
Hanging from the back
The piece of rope beneath the
Water's wave.

*Sarah Webber  (13)*
*Chilton Trinity School*

# MISUNDERSTOOD

I search myself confidently hoping I will find,
Feelings of love within the realms of my mind.
What is love? Is it so close to hate?
Hate; a feeling I love, one showing my fate.

My eyes reveal more than simplicity,
They bring to the surface darkness within me.
Love holds no meaning, but is replaced by lust,
A craving for blood, my knife I don't trust.

I wish not to be evil, nor sinful or bad,
If I controlled my soul I would not feel so sad.
But I drip with life, not that of my own,
Her wounds so deep, so pointless. I am alone.

Do you aid my state? Is there a way?
'I am beyond help' so you lock me away.
Please give me a chance, I wish only to be good,
Cannot you help me?
*I am so misunderstood.*

**Dean Gaylard (15)**
**Chilton Trinity School**


# YOU ARE . . .

As brilliant as a leak in the roof
As a horse with only one hoof
As a knife with no blade
As a handle with no spade. .

As boring as a multiple sum
As a night in, just you and Mum
As a play with no actors
As an English lesson about protractors.

As lonely as Jack without Jill
As a 'went up' without a hill
As a pail with no water
As a suitcase with no porter.

As simple as the 10-times table
As a pot and ladle
As juice in a jug
As an ugly bug.

*Claire McIntyre  (12)*
*Chilton Trinity School*


## THE GLITTER SEA

The gull stays afloat,
On the blue blanket of enchantment,
Soon to strike gold.

The whispering call,
Of nearing wind, tranquil, calm,
As it sweeps the shore.

The sand, soft lightning,
Breaks the foamy wave's boundary,
Swallowing its path.

The spikes of fear,
Surround the prisoned water,
Capturing the surf.

The sand cloud settles,
The sky is glittering with jewels,
The sea rocks gently.

*Jennifer Allen  (12)*
*Chilton Trinity School*

## ZOOM LENS

It is a pile of land stretching from
the horizon to the far distance.
The beach is like a large blanket
with little black dots as patterns.

The sea is lapping fiercely and
roughly upon the golden blanket
reflecting the tall masculine rocks,
like military men lining up
stiffly standing to attention.

Behind them is a beach,
shining from head to toe
like a man in shining armour.

*Sarah Holmes  (12)*
*Chilton Trinity School*


## THE MOON

The moon is a silver coin
falling from heaven
It is a football being kicked
away but always coming back

The moon is a ball of cheese
being eaten slowly
It is a silver bottle top floating
in the dark night sky

The moon is a lighthouse
in a starry night sky
It is a silver blob of paint
on a black piece of paper.

*Natasha Dyte  (13)*
*Chilton Trinity School*

# A HAWAIIAN DREAM

On top of a cliff,
A Hawaiian dream,
Green forests,
Golden sandy beaches,
Clear blue sea,
A dot carrying a white spearhead,
Running towards the sea,
A rolling tube-like wave,
The surfer rides with glee,
The magnificent tube,
Concentration on his face,
The sea calms down,
As the surfer swims out again,
With excitement in his eye,

The sea erupts,
As a huge wave catches the surfer's eye,
Flaming with excitement,
He stands up,
And waves to an imaginary crowd,
Then surfs the great ripple of the sea,
The sea calms down once more,
As the surfer lies on the beach,
With contentment on his face.

*Jonathan Latham  (12)*
*Chilton Trinity School*

## BLIND

I can't explain how I feel
When I go over a hill
In a car or a van
But never the same when I ran.
I don't know what I look like
I don't know do I look right.
With a white stick
I go up town
Is my hair, black, blond, brown?
What do stars look like?
What's it like to ride a bike?
Because I don't know am I asking this right?
I've heard aeroplanes
I can't play games
But I can hear for miles around
I can even hear a penny fall to the ground
What's it like to have a girlfriend?
What's it like to drive around the bend?
Because I don't know 'cause I can't see
My wish would be to see
Maybe, maybe!

*James Ross  (14)*
*Chilton Trinity School*

# PAIN

Pain is fire, so daunting to the flesh,
Seeing her body in the back of my mind,
Smoke all around, yet she does not notice.

A tangled mass of flames and fire,
Screaming out in pain, only to be ignored by
the one who can prevent all of the suffering.

Nerves going numb,
Wanting so desperately for it to be a dream,
Yet no matter how we want, it's reality.

Nobody will listen, nobody will understand,
Soon it'll be over, more than anyone can imagine.

Nobody knows until afterwards, the pain I experience,
Yet still no one understands.

We keep it locked up, for fear of the reaction we
shall receive.

One true friend swallowed up by the sadism
of another.

Yet who can we blame but ourselves?

*Jessica Gascoigne (13)*
*Chilton Trinity School*

## SEA HAIKUS

In the sea of blue
An ancient castle whispers
Its youth of battle.

> The princess of sun
> Fights the prince of all shadows
> On the tranquil sea.

Evil from under
Darkens the world above it
But God sends a light.

> The retired quay
> Lies ragged and deserted
> Weeping for beauty.

*Hannah Woods  (12)*
*Chilton Trinity School*


## THE WATERFALL

The sound of rushing water is quite near
Making sounds that draw you to the weir.

The look of rushing water bubbling white
It makes the day look even more bright.

The smell of rushing water makes you pleased to be here
It makes you realise wildlife is quite near.

The touch of rushing water makes you feel quite calm
You wish the feeling would stay in your palm.

The taste of rushing water doesn't taste
As bad meat that is raw.
It just makes you feel so pure.

*Claire Bamford  (12)*
*Churchill Community School*

## HOMEWORK

Homework, homework, it's always homework,
Maths, English, French and RS,
Why does this homework always get me in a mess?
Homework is boring, it's a waste of time,
Please don't make me go on, I'll just start to whine.
Adding things up and taking away,
I can't deal with this, please just let me go and play.
That's it, I'm off, I'm going away
I'm not doing that homework,
Another boring day!

Paradise and luxury, I've got it all,
Now it's Christmas, the snow starts to fall.
I'm free forever.
It's homework,
'Never!'

*Judy Eastick  (11)*
*Colston's Girls' School*

## RABBITS

I like rabbits, they are fluffy and warm,
They jump and run upon my lawn.
I like rabbits, their ears so long,
Their tails so fluffy that drag on the ground.
My two rabbits, called Smokey and Blossom,
Burrow all day beneath their hutch,
They have gone down very deep,
It's a wonder they haven't already escaped.
My two rabbits Smokey and Blossom.

*Beth Brandford  (11)*
*Colston's Girls' School*

## PUDDLES

I love puddles.
*Splish! Splash! Splosh!*
Hurry, be quick!
The rain's slowing down.
On with my new red wellies
My bright yellow coat
Quick Mum, quick
I want to jump in puddles!

I love puddles!
*Splish! Splash! Splosh!*
Little teeny tiny ones,
They're just a bit splishy.
Big ones are best,
*Splash!*
Yuk!
It's all brown and yukky now.

*Spliish! Splash! Splosh!*
Wow!
A *huge* puddle!
Clear and blue,
Shiny and happy,
It says to me *'Jump!'*
So I do,
Yuk!
I'm all wet and muddy now!
*I hate puddles!*
*Splish! Splash! Splosh!*

***Claire Elliott (11)***
***Colston's Girls' School***

## BOXING BUNNY, BAD CAT!

Into the ring comes Barnaby Rabbit
The boxing bunny from Cromwell's Hide
Circling him is Barney, the bad cat
*Wham! Bam!* Barney goes into strike
Barnaby responds *Wham! Bam!*
A bit of blood. Oooh yuck!
They rest, licking wounds.
They're communicating,
Barney strikes first, *wham!*
Barnaby follows, *bam!*
*Time's up!*
Staggering off both are met by their owners
With the vet checking up (of course!)
. . . *What a fight!*

**Lauren Evers  (11)**
**Colston's Girls' School**


## SISTERS

Sisters. I love them really
Sisters I love them dearly.

When Emily's older she wants to work with vets,
(after all she does love our pets)
When Hannah's older she wants to dance
(to leap, to twirl, to run and prance).

But isn't it so very clear
That to my heart they are so dear?
You get used to their weird and wonderful quirks
And learn to love their cheeky smirks.

> *Sisters, phew!*

**Sarah Doyle  (12)**
**Colston's Girls' School**

# MY TOOTH FAIRY

I saw a smiling face sparkling in the light,
A tiara like a halo sitting on her golden hair,
Her wings feel like rose petals,
they are as blue as the sea,
Her wand she waves sprinkling fairy dust
on my pillow, and me,
Which changes the white ivory tooth
into a silver indented coin,
Then off she goes, bamboozle, she's gone
in a flash of light,
Into the marshmallow clouds in the sky.
But, then I grew older and realised that
the fairy was my mother,
She took my ivory tooth that came out
of my watery mouth,
And even though I know she can't take flight
there's magic there to delight!

*Abigail Barrett  (12)*
*Colston's Girls' School*


# THE PANTHER

Deep in the jungle the panther roams
All his prey he has scattered the bones
The flashing eyes seem to dance
Searching for deer so he can advance.

Up a tree, he starts to eat  .
After, he sleeps in the baking heat.
He stretches his body along the ground
Purring so softly you can't hear a sound.

Another panther comes along
The panther roars as if it were a song
Then the panthers start to fight
But our panther wins because the other was light.

Deep in the jungle the panther roams
All his prey he has scattered the bones
The flashing eyes seem to dance
Searching for deer so he can advance.

*Sarah Gibbs  (11)*
*Colston's Girls' School*

## I DON'T WANT TO GO TO SCHOOL!

Please don't make me go to school Mum,
I really don't want to go.
Let me go back to bed, I want to watch TV.
Please don't make me go to school Mum,
I really don't want to go.

It's a tatty old place,
It's boring,
I hate it there.
Just let me go back to bed,
I'm sure I'll be fine.

Now don't be silly my lamb,
Go and change,
Brush your teeth.
Don't make a fuss,
Now go and catch that *bus!*

*Alice Rose  (12)*
*Colston's Girls' School*

# MY SISTER RACHAEL

My sister Rachael gets up at 8am
From that moment on she is a right pain!
First she watches Pokémon
Then she tells me to put
Cartoon Network on TV
So she can sit and watch with me.

If one of my friends comes to our house
She's always as quiet as a mouse (not!)
She's straight in with - gives me a fright -
'D'y'know what Sarah did last night?
She said a naughty swearing word!'
I ask you, isn't it absurd?

And when it gets to bedtime here -
I think that this is quite unfair -
My little sister, Rachael-Roo
Goes to bed later than I do!
Mind you, I s'pose she doesn't have
To get up as early as I have to
At nearly half-past 6am
So she can start all over again!

*Sarah Melhuish  (11)*
*Colston's Girls' School*

# THE FOUR SEASONS

*Spring*

Spring is when the flowers bloom,
Birds all sing a sweet mellow tune,
Animals come out of hibernation,
All the snow melts across the nation.

*Summer*

Summer's when it's very hot,
People go to the beach a lot,
Some of them go on holiday,
. Off to Majorca or Sandy Bay!

*Autumn*

Autumn's when the leaves fall down,
Some of them go crisp dark brown,
November brings Bonfire Night,
What a glorious whizz-bang sight!

*Winter*

Winter's when the snow falls down,
The birds are gone, you can't hear a sound,
'Christmas is coming' you hear them say,
I can't wait till New Year's Day!

**Carina Powell  (12)**
**Colston's Girls' School**

## CARS

They come in different sizes
And different colours too.
And you can buy the right car
according to you.

Everywhere you look,
And everywhere you go,
There seem to be cars
always on show.

Getting in a new car always smells nice,
But then my mum and dad say,
'Just look at the price.'

My mum wants one car,
My dad wants another,
But I want a Fiat as well as my brother.

*Catherine Wise (11)*
*Colston's Girls' School*


## THE WIND

Blowing, blowing, blowing,
Round and round the wind blows,
Rushing leaves off their feet.

Howling, howling, howling,
Down the chimney the wind howls,
Blowing soot into the room.

Whistling, whistling, whistling,
All day long the wind whistles,
Singing along with the birds.

*Emma Venables (11)*
*Colston's Girls' School*

## BEARS

Bears, bears, everywhere
I think about them all day
In class, in recess
I think of bears.
Angry bears, friendly bears,
Furry, funny, grizzly bears.
I love bears.
Bears, bears, everywhere,
Cuddly toy bears,
They are so amazing.
Big bears, small bears,
I love them all.
Mean bears hate me,
Kind bears love me,
Bears, bears everywhere.
However mean,
However nice,
Fat or thin,
White bears, brown bears,
So many people love them.
So many people hate them.
Bears, bears, everywhere.

*Nicola White  (11)*
*Colston's Girls' School*

## DYSLEXIA

I've always been bad at spelling
Letters are jumbled in my brain
But nobody said I was dyslexic
I never thought I was dyslexic.

I've always been bad at maths
Numbers jumble in my brain
But nobody said I was dyslexic
I never thought I'd be dyslexic.

Then they said I should be tested
A week before the end of school
The results told me what I dreaded
They said I was probably dyslexic.

I was scared what Mum and Dad
Might think but knowing that
My mum is dyslexic made me feel
A bit better.

That night when I got to sleep
I had a nightmare of being bullied about
My dyslexia, it was horrible,
Everybody calling me a dunce and
That I was a waste of space.

I started having lessons with
Mrs Bic to help me with
Spelling and maths.

But now I'm really happy
For being dyslexic,
It's not a problem, just
A way of life so now I've joined
The Dyslexic Club.

*Acacia Boyle (12)*
*Colston's Girls' School*

# HAIR!

If your hair is extremely long,
People can be annoying.
They plait it and twist it,
Flick it and turn it,
I get so frustrated, you wouldn't believe it!

If your hair is extremely short,
You can wash it and style it and dry it.
It bobs and sways,
Doesn't get knotty or fray,
And everyone seems to admire it.

Straight hair is easy to handle,
It's calm and is easy to brush.
Curly hair is wild and it frizzes,
It's really a jungle to brush.

Hair can be a rainbow of colour,
Red, yellow, pink, brown or green.
Highlights and lowlights, glossy and silky,
Mahogany, chestnut and wheat.

When I'm older my hair's going to be
Curly, short, frizzy and green.
Wacky and wild, not carefully styled.
I shall be a sight to be seen!

*Rebecca O'Neill (13)*
*Colston's Girls' School*

## JANUARY

Frost upon the windows,
Snow upon the trees,
Ice upon the puddles,
How my hands do freeze!
Aches in all my fingers
Chilblains on my toes,
Sitting by the fire,
I rub my crimson nose.
In comes Mum with hot chocolate to drink
Now I'm nice and warm,
I'm outdoors and running,
Soon I'm in a glow.

*Hinna Yousuf (12)*
*Colston's Girls' School*


## CHARLOTTE

Charlotte was a delightful child,
with fair hair, soft skin, gentle
and mild.

The passageways brightened up
by her smiles,
her laughter was heard
all around for miles.

Charlotte is someone I could adore,
no one I have ever known has
inspired me more.

*Rose Thomas (13)*
*Frome Community College*

# YOU BELONG TO THE STARS

I will never forget that stagnant smell,
As it maliciously consumed and desecrated
everything in its path.
Stripping a life form of all human response.
Spreading itself through her soft, pasty skin.
It made me cry.
It made her stubborn.
The acceptance was impossible for her,
She would not let go,
Even when her sheets became damp with urine,
And the cup from which she drank was held
not by her hands, but by another's.
She would never let us share her fear.
But I knew that when alone, left with her destroyer
she would weep and scream and tear at the darkness around her.
I could sense, see sometimes, even taste the velvet blanket
of tenebrosity steadily eclipsing her body,
but still she would try to grasp the stars.
I knew now,
that soon new life would brush its warm mouth against hers.
The one tender kiss that would release her.
The one tender kiss that none of us could give to her.
I will never forget that stagnant smell,
But now I know you belong to the stars.

*Yolanda Kaye  (15)*
*Frome Community College*

## AWAKENING

Kneeling by the water
I see myself,
Pure, innocent, fragile.
As I touch the surface, the reflection shatters,
I feel myself drowning again.
Where he touched me my skin goes cold
As the water becomes still deeper.
I struggle to find a safer place,
To break free from the hands which bind me.
I can no longer see the light above me
And darkness offers no comfort.
I try to breathe,
My soul resists it,
Only wanting to escape the memory.
Knowing the end will bring salvation,
Of a kind,
Yet knowing deeper still that the light is still there,
That although I can't see it, it calls out my name.
I know I've been blinded,
I choose now to see,
The demons can never control me again.
I realise they know it,
They see I am changed
And the candle inside me is burning once more.
I have in me the strength to reach up to the surface,
To break through the water and reclaim my life.

Again by the water
I see myself,
Tainted, hurting, scared.

As I touch the surface, the reflection shatters,
But I watch as the image returns.
I see strength shining in me, my mind is awakening,
My soul is my own again.

*Claire Jenner  (17)*
*Frome Community College*


## THE GREAT JOURNEY

I'm just happily running along,
Minding my own business,
Picking up a few leaves on my way,
My great journey, I have a long way to go,
But I will get there.
Suddenly - ouch! A big rock right in the way,
I'm being pushed down,
The pressure over me is enormous,
I try to squeeze through a crack,
Then around the rock,
And then under it,
But it's no use,
I'm pushed up from beneath me,
Up and up and up,
And over the rock,
I'm being dragged over the rock,
And then down the other side,
I've escaped! Back on my journey,
I keep going and know that I will get there;
In the end.

*Emma Clarke  (13)*
*Frome Community College*

## UNTITLED

Distorted visions of modern society
wrapped up warm.
Oblivious to the minority
that sits in the snow
as the world goes 'round.
In my head
In the solar system
Things slowly continue to work
without showing any signs of slowing
Continue to work for the majority,
leaving us out in the snow.

Fear and confusion suppressed
Sat upon by them
left to muddle on in life
Minority loses again.
Cast out, left to die
Continuing our battles
against the fear of majority
and trying to control
the misery and despair
that we are left with
after majority has had its pick.

*Lisa Lanfear  (14)*
*Frome Community College*

## A BOLD WORLD

Insignificantly
    Spiralling
        Onwards
Pain and death and happiness, life twists and distorts
    Further the world
    Rise struggles
        Commitments breaking
    Crawls on in its
           Pointless search.
    Waking a child
        Viciously attacking life's
    Goals
    No different is this star
    If only slightly tainted

And now a pinpoint is
    An eternity
We pass a cottage
    The river
    Ebbs on
Its molecules
Blissfully unaware
    Of the waterfall ahead

        *Tanya*
    A name in a million
    Means so little
    So much
        And nothing.

*Rachael Marchant  (14)*
*Frome Community College*

# FEAR

*What is fear?*

Is it in the films you see?
Or under your dark bed?
Is it in your deep, deep dreams?
Or in your busy head?

*What is fear?*

Is it the shadows from the trees,
In the dead of night?
Or is it the chilly feelings,
Running down your spine?

*What is fear?*

Is it crawling spiders?
Or is it hissing snakes?
Is it a head-on collision,
With only failing brakes?

*What is fear?*

Is it gruesome monsters?
Or is it ghastly ghosts?
Or maybe it's the dark
When your fear is at its most.

*What is fear?*

Fear isn't what you see,
It's more of what you don't.
It's the images you conjure,
When sat all on your own.

**Kylee Guy (14)**
**Frome Community College**

## MY TIME

Time,
My time.
I control my time,
Time does not control me.
I do not rush to keep up with scheduled time.
Therefore, I do not schedule time.
The time is my own.
In that time, I do what I want,
When I want
And how I want.
I make the rules.
What and when I do things,
In my time,
In my place,
Is my choice.
Slowness is a reference to time,
I do things slowly.
Slow is my pace,
My timing.
Lengths of time,
They do not concern me.
My pace may be slow,
Although that does not mean
That my time,
In my place
Is long.
I use that time wisely.
I do not lengthen it,
I do not shorten it.
It is my length,
At my pace,
In my place.
That is my time.

*Nicola Nairne  (14)*
*Frome Community College*

## OUR FUTURE

Silver moons, misty days.
Will we stick to our old ways?
In the future, we will see.

Sunny beaches, salty water.
Will it be the same next year?
When the future is the past.

Fierce wind, raining clouds,
Will they ever disappear?
The future will soon tell.

Green grass, sunny sky.
Will this last forever?
Let's just wait and see.

Misty skies, polluted air,
grey buildings, busy roads.
Will this be our future?

*Rachel George  (14)*
*Frome Community College*


## WHAT'S WRONG WITH ME?

Why can't I speak,
Has the cat got my tongue?
This has never happened before,
It's as though it's been stung.

The way that he smiles,
The way he kicks a ball,
Why can't I just tell him?
I'm being such a fool.

He isn't anything special,
But through my eyes he is.
This has never happened before,
He makes my heart fizz.

I'm going to do it,
Or maybe I won't.
Why can't I just tell him?
God, I hope my friends don't.

**Gemma Curtis  (14)**
**Frome Community College**

## THE JOURNEY

As it stops at the tidy station,
it sighs and puffs while it rests,
its sides heave as it gasps for air.
The paint is intact and no dust can be found
inside or out.
It sits and waits to refill.
Again it heaves itself up and chugs along.
It breathes heavily,
smoke drifting across the sky.
From sunset to sunrise and sunrise to sunset
it struggles along the metal track.
Day after day, night after night,
it has an ongoing journey,
ongoing journey,
ongoing,
ongoing.

**Laylah McGregor  (13)**
**Frome Community College**

## SPINE CHILLER

It's a cold winter day.
White breath pours out of my mouth,
Like smoke.
My trainers crunch loudly
Against the gravel drive.
The sound echoes around,
Hits the towering walls of the Manor.

Hugging my fleece around me,
I hurry up the path,
Place the old, rusty key in the lock and turn it.
The large wooden door swings open
With a low-pitched creak.
As I step inside, a shiver creeps up my spine.
Suddenly,

The old door slams shut,
I feel a presence in the room,
I'm frozen to the spot,
Something stirs in the gloom.

A soft, cold hand brushes my shoulder.
As I run, I hear a voice,
'Don't go, don't leave, stay, help me!'
But I don't stay.
I run, I flee.

*Karen Chilvers  (13)*
*Frome Community College*

# HE'S NOT AFRAID

Searching through the undergrowth, looking for bamboo shoots,
Many different plants, including fern and tall Redwood roots.
A shiny mat of glistening, reflective fur, as strong as a prominent beast
Lying lazily on the back of a mountainous piste.
The humid atmosphere lingers along the trees
Waiting to rise to swarm the sky as a refreshing, cool breeze.
A motionless array of life rests on the carpeted floor
Dreaming, in succession of work, they can handle no more.
An abrupt eruption of echoing noise makes the strong, agile beast's
ears ring

He's not afraid of anything.
A crunch of leaves as footsteps continually scurry
He's not afraid, it gives him no worry.
A squelch of mud as something lies down
He's not afraid as he gives a slight frown.
Silence as the ears can perceive an eerie sound
He's not afraid, he's standing his ground.
An alloy shaft takes its aim
He's not afraid of the wind and the rain.
A short, sharp shock ripples through the animal's chest
He's afraid, afraid of the end of the rest.
He lies on the ultimate place of his existence . . . dead
Growing colder as he bled.
Hapless Mountain Gorilla, a lifeless heap
As death arrives eager to reap.
The killer so satisfied at what he created
Life and death are always debated.

*Myles Painter  (13)*
*Frome Community College*

## SCARED TO DREAM

I've seen things that I shouldn't have seen.
I've been places that I shouldn't have been.
And I'm scared to dream,
Scared to think of what things may seem,
And when I wake up the feeling's still there.
My T-shirt clings to my hair, sweat forces my skin
To cling to hair
And it plays over in my head
As I lie there, sheets falling off my bed.
In my dream, my sister
Turns my head to utter some unimportant words to someone.
She didn't see it coming, nor hear it
As she was tossed into the air.
Lying there lifeless.
I'll never forget that moment.
The reason for my insomnia.
I can't sleep,
I'm afraid to dream.
I've seen things I shouldn't have seen.

*Cara Holt  (13)*
*Frome Community College*


## THE SHARK

The sleek, streamlined body,
those gaping jaws of death,
it swims through the water
like a bullet through the air.

A small, colourful ray
laying on the seabed,
a flick of the tail
and this little ray is no more.

A fisherman bringing up an eel,
this little eel is about to become lunch,
the speeding shark like a big torpedo,
hitting the eel with the force of a bomb.

The line goes tight and the drag screams,
people on the boat wait in wonder.
A few hours later and a shark on the boat.
'Not bad,' said the fisherman, 'it put up quite a fight.'

***Dominic Emery  (14)***
***Frome Community College***


## VOICES OF BOYS

In a field many miles away,
The poppy-lined grass shivers and shakes,
Where, from the earth the echoes seep,
Spinning and shaking, a search to be free.

The voices of boys,
A chorus of questions, rasping and choking,
They fly, high on the wings of doves.

Crowded cities heave with the pounding of vibrating streets,
All lives crushed into one metal can,
Motionless faces hide clamouring feelings,
Deep inside they're so scared
As they claw to the future,
A future of high-rise promises that increase by the second,
Promises of Utopia when the anger has ceased.

In a field many miles away,
A scarlet petal quivers.

***Rosanne White  (14)***
***Frome Community College***

# FUTURE

Bright lights, loud noises, great big clumps of smog,
The technology can make flying cars travel at the speed of sound.
Robots are doing the TV shopping for us
And phoning our friends on the 3000 AD Internet.
Machines taking over the human population.
The walls enclosing, close, keeping us prisoners in this VR world.
Computerised test-tube babies, half human, half animal.
Changing our faces at the touch of a button.
Computers with a mind of their own.
Nuclear bomb scares in every corner of this world.
Half-week vacations to the Red Planet.
Will the world end while I'm alive, or when you're alive?

*Tina Wakefield  (13)*
*Frome Community College*


# DREAMS

I dream that I once had
was full of all things good and bad.
Things floated in and out of my mind,
of answers for questions that I could not find.
Things dark and light flashed by
as I wondered how I would die.
I think of stories that I've been told
and how the people were so brave and bold,
and soon the hours slipped into minutes
and seconds fell upon, as slowly
I went into a deep, deep sleep.
And soon enough I woke up thinking
'Oh Monday week!'

*Jenny Preston  (14)*
*Frome Community College*

# I REMEMBER ...

I remember my grandpa,
he used to tell jokes
and make me laugh.
He used to point out my family
in their baby photographs.

I remember playing with Barbies
and my sister tearing off their heads,
making me cry.
I really thought Bikini Barbie
was going to *die!*

· I remember tears and tantrums
when my mum didn't believe
my sordid tales of eeriest spooks
and large, white phantoms.

I remember when I was in playschool,
learning my ABCs,
playing with my little friends
with bruises all over my knees.

I remember ...

*Fae Palmer  (13)*
*Frome Community College*

## THE FUTURE

In the future, in times to come
When I have been
A child,
A teenager,
An adult,
A mum,
I will find that times of
Writing
And walking
And talking
Are only in my mind,
Reality is a place of competition,
Computers,
Shopping on-line
And the overwhelming loss of jobs making many revert to crime,
Mass murders,
Terrorist attacks
Bomb raids and rape
Along the line
Will become an every day part of life.
Every person will know another who is connected
To this strife.
A finger will not be lifted for the stretch of a week,
For technology will be the very centre of our lives.
Even simple tasks
Such as turning on the shower
Will be computerised.
But, until this time, *take* time to do the easy things;
You will regret it once the chance is gone.

*Philippa Hirst  (13)*
*Frome Community College*

## THE WAVES

The waves are what I see when I go to the sea,
The waves are what I see when I swim,
The waves are what I feel when I dive in,
The waves splash down like white horses,
The waves are what people surf on,
The waves are like a roller-coaster,
The waves are like a watery liquid,
The waves are like a new wave in a world of fashion,
The waves become extremely dangerous,
The waves are like a process of waving hair,
The waves are like a body of water curling into an
arched form and breaking on the shore,
The waves are a specified period of widespread weather,
The waves to me are the new flower blossoming.

*Louisa Lowe  (13)*
*Frome Community College*


## DAYS TO COME

Screaming fiercely,
it's just around the corner.
In the hands of a crystal ball
lies our future.

What can we see?
What will happen next?
Down which path will life take us?
Through the good times into the bad,
love, happiness, cheerful days,
depression, loneliness all of these ways,
wait for the days to come.

*Catherine Reynolds  (14)*
*Frome Community College*

## HOME?

My birthplace and home for eight years,
soaring skyscrapers,
venerable flats on the horizon.
The dirty harbour, once fragrant,
now diseased and smelly from decades of abuse.

The racing course below,
minute from above, complete with children's playground.
Cars in insect form scuttle and yell in exasperation,
tooting all hours of day and night.

Kung Hei Fat Choi!
The dragon would stamp out.
Lanterns, fireworks and Lai See.
Poinsettias and kumquats,
crowning the empty swimming pool in gold and red.

Suffocating walls of people,
surrounding you in the mall,
surrounding you in the market,
surrounding you in the street.
A tidal wave.

Now things may be different,
Chris Patten, left.
Only few friends remain.
No longer the island we recognise,
Barely a pinpoint on the map.
Hong Kong.

*Naomi Hirst (13)*
*Frome Community College*

## PREDATOR OF THE NIGHT

The dinosaur arched its back and roared.
The dark night was closing in and with the dark, something else.
Lurking in the trees, the dinosaur smelt its doom.
Trying in vain to get away, it blundered and in its confusion,
                                                went the wrong way.

Snap, crack, all over.
Broken, bloody, the body lies.
Another strip of flesh is torn from the once mighty dinosaur.
Another roar breaks the gloom and the predator steps out.
Soon this proud king of the dinosaurs will be dead,
Killed by a massive meteorite obscuring all life
Little knowing that millions of years later,
Humans will try to de-throne him,
Tyrannosaurus Rex, once king of the dinosaurs,
Now is preserved in stone.

*Robert White  (13)*
*Frome Community College*


## A FRIEND?

It annoys me how she mimics, criticises and lies to me.
Vicious lies, lies of hatred and greed,
which causes me grief and pain.
Competing with me, over ridiculous measures,
possessing me, to get the highest A* grade,
when all I want is to escape from this dilemma.
This anger she has trapped, buried deep into her heart.
Is the jealousy here to stay? I beg not as it . . .
kills, murders and tears me greatly inside,
when all I need is a caring, trusting, true friend.

*Farrah Staples  (14)*
*Frome Community College*

## THERE IS NO TREAT!

As I walk through the park,
I see a dog.
He looks at me, with his gloomy eyes
looking very sad and glum.
His eyes follow my hand
thinking there's a treat waiting for him,
but there's not.
So I pick up a stick
and throw it.
His gloomy eyes follow,
he bounds away,
retrieves the stick,
looks around,
but I'm gone.

*Paul Warder  (15)*
*Frome Community College*


## EXCEPTIONS TO THE RULE

Achieve?
'I' before 'E' except after 'P'.
No.
'I' before 'C' except after Me.
No, no.
'E' before 'I' except after Pie.
No, no, no.
Breakfast before lunch, except after brunch.
No way.
'I' before 'E' except . . .
I'll use 'Attain'!

*Nick Sealy  (14)*
*Frome Community College*

## DREAMS

In an untamed corner of my mind,
I slowly drift up and away,
to somewhere far in the distance.
My mind lets go and I gently float by . . .
arriving somewhere else,
where everything is free;
the gentle breeze,
the warm sun,
the silent hum of the birds.
I quietly listen
and yet I cannot hear a single voice,
shout or scream.
This is a place of happiness,
freedom and peace;
a place where dreams happen,
and still,
no matter how hard I try
to adapt to this new place,
I can never completely let go, because,
dreams are something special,
things that you sink in to,
taking them as they come . . .
Dreams, dreams, dreams.

*Vicki Ayres  (13)*
*Frome Community College*

## THE SUN

The immense fiery presence,
As small as the gap between your eyes,
Although up close the everlasting spirit
Seems so unreal,
With the anger of an agitated gorilla,
And the vastness of an ant in a desert plain.
It would appear extraordinarily baffling
That it is as shy as a hunted fox,
Especially as the coal black blanket extinguishes
The lively, fresh daylight remains.
The tortoise loiters from snow-white bush to bush,
As it likes to play games.
Alas, do not glare at this fireball
That is the sun.

*Simon Lynn  (13)*
*King Edward's School*


## NIGHT-TIME

It comes without warning.
Creeping over, it quiets the birds in the trees.
A black carpet of emptiness which
scares those who dare to cross its path.
It will provide no light, except that of the
twinkling fire as it sends the sun away.
It will stay until the cock crows,
but it will not go away.
As it moves on to haunt more unexpecting victims,
it will bring out only the brave
and will never be defeated.

*Edward Randle  (13)*
*King Edward's School*

# THE SKY

The sky is like a lady's coat,
it drags in puddles and gets wet
and she has to rinse it out.
She puts on a black cloak
with beads in that reflect the light.
She puts on a blue coat
with a yellow spot and grey areas
where it has faded.
There is sometimes a hole in the coat
and the light shines through.
At the end of the day, the colour
runs to an orange or red,
so she buys a new cloak
for the start of the day.

*Sam Sheppard (13)*
*King Edward's School*


# BULLET

She slides perfectly through the smooth shaft,
as if it were made of marble.
As fast as lightning, she shoots off like a thunderbolt.
She flies like a bat out of hell.
Down the misty, gloomy tunnel of darkness
towards death and destruction,
cutting through the air like a knife through butter,
then, impact.
Piercing screams of pain and terror.
It cripples whatever blocks its path.
Thick streams of red flow,
then silence.

*Henry Williamson (14)*
*King Edward's School*

## WATER

Water creeping,
slowly downhill.
Rippling over stones, trapped,
in the river bed.
Suddenly, it picks up speed,
faster and faster and faster
as it reaches the edge,
eager to see what is down below.
It keeps on going as if it didn't
get a close enough look, following
its friends like a flock of sheep,
and then hits the water waiting
for it below with a thunder-like
rumble as it creates a lather
of bubbles on the surface,
and
then,
it
decreases
in speed
and continues its journey to the furious sea.

*Neil Campbell  (13)*
*King Edward's School*


## SCHOOL

The school bell rang,
It was time to go,
The children ran,
Through the snow.

They then sat down
To eat their lunch,
Whilst watching children
Play and punch.

The bell rang again
So they came in from play
All covered in bags
To restart the day.

The bell rang again
For the very last time
And all the children went home
To dine.

*James Burrell  (12)*
*King Edward's School*


## THE UNLIKELY ESCAPE

The fish had been landed,
One thing was clear,
His days were over, permanently over.
The scales were glinting in the sun,
as a coat of armour would.
Although this had done it no good.
Its gills, pumping relentlessly, found no oxygen.
The eyes had already begun to cloud and
stared aimlessly into those of the angler.
He would soon be busy apprehending his next victim.
His whole body writhed continuously
deep in the folds of the net.
As the last glimmer of life
was about to leave the exasperated gills,
The angler gave a heavy sight and as death loomed large
relinquished the fish as nimbly as an elephant.
The water's surface was shattered for a split-second,
but as the ripples faded - calm returned.

*Nicholas Connolly  (13)*
*King Edward's School*

## MY GOLDFISH!
*(Dedicated to my goldfish)*

Trapped in the shiny, clear water,
Caged with nowhere to hide,
My fish emerges quick as a beat,
Hungry, longing for food he has spied.

His small, scrawny once-golden complexion,
Has turned grey in his old age,
But hasn't slowed his lightning speed or
dimmed his love for his reflection.

He swims idly around as if he has no brain,
As if he has no recollection of his life so plain.
He had a dear companion, but now that fish has died.
All he has now is water weed that sways from side to side.

I feed many crispy flakes
As he bangs his head again and again against the side,
The flakes sink to the bottom like snowflakes falling from the sky.
He's still trying to break his nose as his lunch goes sailing by.

*Jessica Ost  (12)*
*King Edward's School*


## TELEVISION

Television can make you laugh like a clown in a Big Top.
Television can make you bored like an RE class in school.
Television can make you cry like if someone pinched you
                                        really hard.
Television is a hyena.
Television is an owl.
Television is what you watch with your friend.
Television drives your mother round the bend.

*Craig Borland  (13)*
*King Edward's School*

## THE COLOURFUL DRAGON

He wraps himself around the peak of the highest mountain,
The colours shining off his tail
creating a rainbow through the pouring rain,
The rain as it splashed around him.

His scaly body is entwined around his
treasure like a curled-up snake,
He gathers it up in his tail and flies
away,
Over the sea to a far-off land,
Because he knows the valiant soldier
is coming.

*William Jones (12)*
*King Edward's School*


## THE OLD MAN

The old man was as old as the oak tree.
His knowledge a bottomless pit.
He looks at his car which he can no longer drive.
She had wheels which were more rusty than rust.
The red paint was chipped and the windows cracked.
The old man sighed.
His head was bald and as smooth as marble.
His teeth were as crooked as a corkscrew,
and some were missing.
His skin was as a desert.

*Tom Jones (13)*
*King Edward's School*

## PARK LIFE

The frosted sunlight
Comes filtering through
The chestnut tree.

The spider watches
The world from her
Crystallised web.

She sees the blackbird
Take two, three hops
Over the frost,
And stop to preen its feathers
Into glassy perfection.

The smoke scented air
Hangs drunkenly over
The sleepy morning.

The silvered sky is scarred
By a single white blur.

*Kate Clark  (12)*
*King Edward's School*


## BLADES OF GRASS

Blades of grass are tiny, green knives,
Glistening in the sun like glinting blades.
They wave in the breeze and whisper as they sway,
As if to compose sweet serenades.
They are the bed of the insect that sleeps in the sun.
They are the lawn of the garden where the children run.
They are the green of the fields with buttercups and blooms.
They are the inspiration of artists as they paint from their rooms.

*Lewis Topley  (13)*
*King Edward's School*

## THE LEAVES

The
leaves
shuddered
as the breeze
flew past, then waved
as if they were water
lapping over the pebbled
shore of an autumn lake.
They quivered as the gusts
grew strong and seemed to
float like bubbles, drifting aimlessly.
Then suddenly, the leaves like sheets
of gold as they caught the sun
beams, in a stream of air were
plucked from their beds in the
arms of a chestnut. They
flittered to the ground
like dandelion seeds,
and the tree
was bare
once
more.

*Ella Morison  (13)*
*King Edward's School*

# THE SEA

The sea slowly crawled up the beach
As the waves swayed like trees in a breeze.
Then the wind howled like a wolf in the woods.
As the waves crashed down like the roar of a lion,
The sea beat against the rocks
And the boats were tossed and turned.
Now all is calm and the buoys bob like apples.
The sea is clear and as blue as the sky.
The seagulls soar like planes
As the dolphins flit and glide.
The trees on the coast wave like flags in the wind
As the sun goes down for the day to end.

*Louise Fisher  (13)*
*King Edward's School*


# SOMEWHERE

I can't help to think of things beyond the prison walls,
beyond the tallies and desperate calls,
beyond the grey and iron bars,
how I would love to see the moon and stars.
All bright colours are beyond my sight,
it's hard to tell whether it's day or night,
a dingy smell looms in the air,
there is nothing to do except stare.
Is there life beyond the walls?
I wish I could put right my flaws,
all these things I have forgotten,
this life is rotten.

*Gavin Leesam  (12)*
*King Edward's School*

## BEHIND THE OLD DOOR

A silence hung over them,
Sarah began to count to ten,

Then she let it all out,
The silence was broken by a shout.

'It's not fair,'
'Why should I be the one to go in there?'

The three children had a fight,
Then Sarah pushed open the door with all her might,

Then she ran out as if she had seen a bat,
The boys laughed, it was only a cat.

They all burst through the door,
The ceiling was dusty, so was the floor.

Then Sarah tripped over a broom,
After all that it was just an old storeroom.

*Eleanor-Louise Kenning  (12)*
*King Edward's School*


## THE LONELY TREE

He sways from side to side in whistling wind
like a dog's tail when it's happy.
His leaves rustle against each other
as plastic bags do when they're scrumpled.
As the wind gets stronger, the anger in him grows
as the light-weight leaves fly all over the place.
The wind drops and he becomes as calm
as the sea on a hot, summer's day.

*David Hoare  (13)*
*King Edward's School*

## HAPPILY MISERABLE

I am happily miserable.

My pen gives a plastic, rattled yell,
As I throw it down on wooden ground.
And I stare hard at the large pile of non-existent homework
Then look across to the non-existent pile of done homework.

That is why I am miserable?

Suddenly, the hall is filled with the sound of laughter,
Like a group of hyenas who have just eaten somebody,
An onlooker would have caught,
'Did you see his face!' or
'He was all over the place!'
I am with that group.

That is why I am happy?

There is still something pulling me down,
Down from the height of happiness.
Down to the depths of misery,
Where I will scream inside at no one, everyone and everything.
Where tears will well but I will never quite cry.

The balloon inside me is continually being dragged down
Dragged by a clenched fist.
I feel the fist.

I wonder why I am happily miserable.

*Madeline Coleborn (12)*
*King Edward's School*

## THE SECRET

As I stared spellbound into the night
The dark grew silent
I wished for noise, something to awaken me
From this dark, dreaded nightmare.

I felt eyes watching me.

As I stared bleakly around me
Like an eagle searching - for its prey.
Ahead of me, I saw a glimpse of light.

Red eyes startled me from the corner of my eye
Its eyes as red as fire,
Blazing in the dark of the night.

I felt a powerful force around me,
It burnt me,
Like a needle jabbing through my heart.

Although I did not, I had a reason to run,
To run from this nightmare,

But inside me, I had a willingness to stay,
As if I was being allured by the power.

As if the beast I felt before me held the answer.

The answer to the dark, magical secret of the future.

*Anna Brownrigg  (13)*
*King Edward's School*

# MYSTERY

On the top of Misty Hill
Stands a castle, forlorn and still.
Inside those dark and gloomy walls,
Lie mysteries that would enthral.

Like a million birds flying over the tower,
Fell a shadow which held some unknown power,
The shadow flowed through the door
And changed into the shape of a wild boar.

Into the hallway it trotted with glee,
Tonight is the night to give thanksgiving to he,
He the overlord of the animals and creatures,
And now he enters with his beautiful features.

Into the room strode a bear in a gown,
And on top of his head lay a twinkling great crown.
He roared in pleasure to see his followers here,
Then he shouted in a bold voice, 'Have no fear!'

His followers at once knew the mission was done,
At last the battle had been won.
They left the castle in a triumphant way,
For today they had put the enemy at bay.

*Sam Dawson  (12)*
*King Edward's School*


# 'TIS I

Down, down the mountain I do go,
With clothes all tattered covered in snow.
Swooshing down,
Face in a frown.
'Tis I who will never die.

Now the winter's drawing to a close,
With trees all white covered in snow
The snows all a-melt,
But still down I pelt
'Tis I who will always live.

*John McBride  (12)*
*King Edward's School*


## ESCAPE!

In the beginning there was the world;
In the future will come the planets . . .

Neptune, Venus, Jupiter -
But it is on Mars the scene will be set.
'Humans have been slaves for too long!
Set us free!'
Astra sought the King's ear.
'Let us go!'
'Never!' the King shouted.
Lightning struck and water turned to ice . . .
'Never will I let my slaves go!'
Again, lightning struck and the Martians' skin began to flake.
'Never!' the King raged.
Lightning struck for the final time and the Martian daughters gasped
their last breaths, fading into dust.
The King granted the slaves a spaceship and set them free.
But the Humans' hopes faded as they saw a great asteroid belt.
Suddenly, there was a bright flash of light as the asteroid belt parted.
Meanwhile the King was advancing on them, making rapid progress.
As the Martians passed through the asteroid belt
The gap closed and they were crushed.

Future voices in past's firm hold.

*Andrew White  (12)*
*King Edward's School*

# Autumn Glory

Walking under the crisp blue sky,
There is a dark black shadow,
It is of the old oak tree which sways about in the wind.
The leaves are dry and brown like an old man's face.
It creaks and cracks and I think it might fall over.
Also on the nearly bare tree,
There are some green spiky things,
With a fruit inside.
It is all dark and brown and shiny,
We play with them on strings and try to hit
each other's off.
To see who wins.

When all the leaves have fallen off
And all the conkers have gone
The tree looks bare but wonderful
In a very different way,
You see all the lovely shapes of the twigs
But in a couple of months,
The tree will regain its colour on the creaky old tree.

*Tim Wagstaff (12)*
*King Edward's School*


# The Orchestra

The violins are getting ready to start their adventure,
The horn is blowing to start the battle,
The flutes are the bow and arrows,
The conductor lifts his baton.

The cellos are playing to the beat of the men's hearts,
The clarinet represents the adrenaline,
The drums are the cannons,
The conductor lifts his baton.

The oboes are the horses running through the wood,
The trumpets announce the arrival of the king,
The violas are the swords,
The conductor lifts his baton.

The leader walks up to the sound of gunfire,
The conductor walks up to a flash of lightning,
The orchestra gets ready for the battle to start,
The conductor lifts his baton.

*Tom Hamilton  (12)*
*King Edward's School*


## THE WORLD

The tiny snail looks up at the stars,
While the huge aeroplane looks down on the cars,
Mother crocodiles protect their eggs,
While emus run on long thin legs.

As the world turns.

Eagles are certainly not weak,
As they can kill deer with their sharp beak.
In the world there is so much pollution,
And at the moment there is no solution.

As the world turns.

The population of the world is great,
Does each person have a fate?
The world is incredibly vast and wide,
But there will be nothing left if a
Comet should collide.

As the world stops.

*George Glen  (12)*
*King Edward's School*

## THE BIRD

The bird swooped and soared through the morning air.
The sun reflecting off his golden wings.
His yellow beak slashing at the nearest seeds,
waiting expectantly to be eaten,
like a mouse after a cat has spied it.
A rainbow with its endless colours falling away to infinity.
The last points of the stars finally blinking out.
The full moon still just seen in the sky. The clouds splitting apart.
The sun rising in the sky.
The bird glided through a cloud and into the rainbow
and was lost in the endless colours.

*Charles Barter  (12)*
*King Edward's School*


## FOREST FIRE

As the sun gazed down on the lime coloured grass,
I can hear noises.
The sounds of trees rustling and animals bustling
with insects crawling in-between.
As the sounds of crackling and the screeching
like a peacock, came from the stillness of the forest.
The ash type smoke covered the field as if a storm
was brewing.
And as the orange flames soared higher into the sky,
burning everything in its path.
Then the monstrous flames died down leaving us
nothing but the scorched black grass.

*Louise Knight  (12)*
*King Edward's School*

## PLEASE MRS JOHNSON

Please Mrs Johnson,
I don't know what to do,
There's not a thought in my head,
I just haven't got a clue!

All you need is inspiration,
And a wild imagination.
Don't forget determination,
And a little application.

Please Mrs Johnson
I really cannot think.
I haven't got a rubber,
And my pen's run out of ink.

It won't cause you aggravation,
It won't bring you irritation,
If you use your concentration
And a little dedication.

Sorry Mrs Johnson
I don't know what I lack,
This poem thing is not for me,
I haven't got the knack!

*Katharine Pooley  (12)*
*King Edward's School*

## MY DOG

He walks into the room,
All alert,
Sniffing, listening and watching,
Then he looks at you with those big brown eyes,
They pierce you like a knife through butter.
Your heart begins to flutter,
You know what he wants,
He knows you'll finally succumb,
To his wondrous gaze,
It sets you all ablaze,
And all he wants is a morsel of that luscious fruit cake.

But a piece is not enough
He begins to drool
It makes a pool,
Just at your feet,
So tidy and neat,
If he doesn't get what he wants from you he'll get it
From someone else.

You fall into his trap as you have done so many times,
You give him another piece,
But now you've finished,
It's as hard to tell him you've finished than a split up with
Your girlfriend,
So you're almost forced to get some more,
He follows you even though he's got a limp,
Just for a morsel of food.

*Matthew Tupper  (12)*
*King Edward's School*

## TIME

Some people have it,
Some people keep it,
Some people want it,
Some people need it.

Some people waste it,
Some people use it,
Some people spend it,
Some people lose it.

You can't go back in it,
You can't travel through it,
You can't change it,
You can't stop it.

Past,
Present,
Future,
Think about how much you have.

*Edward Hollis  (12)*
*King Edward's School*

# DARK BUT NOT QUITE BLACK

The last hint of light is enveloped,
Folded and sealed in the night.
Glittering pinpricks in the swirling fabric,
Dark but not quite black!

The air is slightly chilled by early frost
And midnight crystals slowly grow in clusters.
As time chews away at the unrevealing darkness,
The first movement is heard!

Although my sight tells nothing,
I sense the midnight creatures now awake
For our night is their day
And our day is their night.

Then a bubble of light emerges,
And the glass enchantment is broken.
Screams and shouts of another day,
Future voices of the morning.

***Emma Cullen  (13)***
***Kings of Wessex School***

# COULDN'T FIT IT ALL IN

The unisexed but multitalented homosapiens.
In the undergrowth they crawl.
In swarms of wire cables covered in gangrene.
Enclosed by chicken wire heated so hot it drawls.
The plate at the front tells the story *'See them for yourself!'*

American tourists crowd fatly to one side.
Tour guides, aliens, wizards and the cults,
All with 45-inch semi-automatics.
All closely behind one another,
Nits jump from body to body, field day.
On the locomotive, so artistically designed.

Special groups of humans
Spiritualist healers, NASA, pyromaniacs
And their sniffer dogs, pirates from the sky,
Underground pilots, spiritualists, vets,
The Queen surrounded by her lover-bodyguards
Song lyrics sung by the original artists.

A mobile phone rings,
Mass search now on,
Locomotive strains under designer shoes.
Miss two stops,
Go back to go and collect fifty pounds.

*Oliver Morris  (15)*
*Kings of Wessex School*

## ISBN

Nice outer.
Deceiving!

A page, a page;
An infinitely complex monotony,
I had said.

Seems the same - identical picture,
In light, not ink;
Engraved; not embossed,
The sandpaper of time has little effect.

Words along the line,
Meander, shortcut.

What I was destined to be, I will never become.
Perpetual enhancement
Got in the way.

Acknowledgements to an
Unknown wife,
And someone named God.

*Joe Woodburn  (15)*
*Kings of Wessex School*

## I HAD A DREAM ONCE

I had a dream once,
That our houses had stories,
Speaking in unknown, dust-clogged tongues
Their secrets come slithering
From every timbered crack,
Steadfast, sentinels,
Against the frozen wastes of the future,
The confused blur of white noise,
Making sense of jigsaw-puzzled lives within,
Black and white memories hang,
Poised like crystals inside stone-encased spirits,
Casting rainbows
I had a dream once . . .

*Jennifer Wainwright  (13)*
*Kings of Wessex School*


## EMANCIPATION OF WOMEN

E   mancipation of women
M   arching through the streets,
A   n alliance of women
N   one of them would eat.
C   hained to railings
I   nsolidarity they unite,
P   roud of their gender
A   nd the necessary fight.
T   he vote was won at last
I   n 1918,
O   nly married women over 30
N   ow I think that was mean!

*Jessica Simpson  (12)*
*Norton Hill School*

## FANTASY

When ostriches flew and trees walked
And fruit grew upon thorn
Some moment when the fishes were winged
That was when I was born.

Born of fairy stock
Underneath the blood-red moon
Born in the month
Of the starlit hune.

Our voices like the birds' song,
My laughter, the bubble of a stream,
Innocent and full of mischief,
Our steps light as the moon's beam.

When a baby claps her hands
It is us she does see
Do you see the ferns curled?
That is the handiwork of me.

Should you seek to find us,
Then look around!
We are in the child's laughter
In the first icy frost on the ground.

We fairy folk are merry
Lo! We dance with glee
And when day's fingers grab the sky
We gather and flee.

*Aileen Bachrach  (13)*
*Norton Hill School*

## THAT WAS THE CENTURY THAT WAS

T  he first Ford was manufactured in 1903
H  urricanes are becoming more frequent,
A  lbert Einstein invented the light bulb,
T  elephone was invented in 1876.

W  e won the World Cup in 1966,
A  eroplanes fly people all around the world,
S  aab make aeroplanes, cars and trucks.

T  ransport has improved but roads are more dangerous,
H  omeless people live in shop doorways, and on the street,
E  lephants are becoming endangered due to hunting.

C  oca Cola can be used for cleaning old coins,
E  arthquake hits Turkey in September 1999
N  eil Armstrong was the first man in space,
T  elevision was invented in 1926,
U  nicycles are one wheel bicycles,
R  edcoats (Guides) became famous at Butlins,
Y  ellow submarine was a big hit for The Beatles.

T  ape recorders were invented in 1935
H  ospital waiting lists are getting bigger,
A  lexander Graham Bell invented the telephone
T  itanic hit the bottom on 2.30am April 15th 1912.

W  orld War Two started in 1939
A  dolph Hitler started World War Two
S  teven Spielberg's the worlds most successful film maker.

*Brad Whittock  (12)*
*Norton Hill School*

## GOODBYE TO THE TWENTIETH CENTURY

Goodbye to the twentieth century
Are you happy to see it go?
When Concorde was invented
And Titanic went down below.

These are two disasters
There are good things as well
In World War Two when the
Population fell.

Now let me tell you about something good
Like computers and cars
And when they sent a satellite
To investigate Mars.

*Sarah Macey (11)*
*Norton Hill School*


## 20TH CENTURY

The twentieth century is nearly gone,
A lot of things have happened.
For good and for bad,
Two World Wars, the rise of Adolph Hitler.
Tragedies like Princess Diana and J F Kennedy
Achievements like the first man on the moon.
Rights for women and black people.
Technological advances like TV, radio, PCs
And the Internet.
But with all this success there is still famine,
Disease and homelessness.

*Daniel Lambert (12)*
*Norton Hill School*

## GOODBYE TO THE TWENTIETH CENTURY

Goodbye to the twentieth century
It's sad to see it go
We've had World War One and World War Two
The Gulf War and Vietnam.

The first woman Prime Minister
Girl Power hits the world.
Titanic sank alas, alas!
Hong Kong goes back to China.

Computers, aeroplanes, microwave ovens,
Telephones, TV, the lot!
Royal marriages what galore,
Balloon around the world.

Global warming, the greenhouse effect.
Hitler - what a villain!
World Cup 1966
England are the champs!

The world has changed in mysterious ways,
Like mad cow disease, The Beatles,
J F Kennedy, a terrible tragedy,
Concorde was invented.

Space satellites, what amazing machines
Hurricane fever.
And we will never forget
When man first went to the moon.

*Adele Wright  (11)*
*Norton Hill School*

# GOODBYE TO THE TWENTIETH CENTURY

As the twentieth century will soon be gone,
These are something's that it means to me.
I'm glad, glad of the invention of the telephone,
Why? I can talk to my friend whenever I like,
Car! I can go wherever I like, whenever I like.
I'm glad of TV, I can watch all of the soaps,
The news is interesting, but sometimes tragic,
Like the Turkish earthquakes
Over ten thousand people died,
We can be grateful, there isn't too big a possibility for us.
Princess Diana's death in the car chase, people crying.
One of the most publicised events was probably
The two World Wars, millions killed, peace is now upon us.
Finally the most memorable event is
landing on the moon.
These are just a few of the big events
that have happened in the 20th century.

*Samantha Newman  (12)*
*Norton Hill School*


# EARTHQUAKE

The cracking sound
Of breaking ground
And the loud pound
Of falling houses.
Fatal screams fill the air
Fires start with a sizzling flare,
The running footsteps of frightened kids,
Not knowing where to go.
What will the town look like tomorrow?
Will I live to know?

*Becky Pearce  (12)*
*Norton Hill School*

## PLEASE DON'T TAKE ME

Please don't take me to the dentist,
Please don't take me to the nurse,
Please don't take me to the doctors,
I think I'd rather get worse.

Please don't take me on holiday,
Please don't take me to the zoo,
Please don't take me to the seaside,
I don't want to go with you.

Please don't take me swimming,
Please don't take me to school,
Please don't take me to tennis,
I think I'd rather play ball.

*Alone.*

***Penelope Roberts  (12)***
***Norton Hill School***


## CARS

I'm glad cars have been invented
Although don't you find they're always dented,
I hate the noisy banged up old ones
You know the ones that go about as fast as a sloth when it runs,
I like cool cars like Aston Martin
Cool, they're are fast, have you seen them darting?
There are soft tops, Ferraris and stretch limos
And tiny Minis the size of minnows,
There are BMWs, coaches and lorries,
And there are Datsons, they've got to say some sorrys.

***Jonathon Hoare  (12)***
***Norton Hill School***

# Goodbye To The Twentieth Century

I cheered when Man Utd did the treble,
Thank goodness for electricity
Beatles, Elvis, Wet Wet Wet and Offspring.
Bring music to my ears via Walkmans.
Equipped with mobile phones and the Internet,
Freedom has only just begun.

Sadness reminds us of icons,
Such as J F Kennedy, Elvis and Lennon,
And our great loss Princess Diana,
Her warmth will surely be missed by millions.

We overcame two World Wars,
Man walked on the moon,
McDonalds went to Russia,
Channel tunnel finally achieved,
Millennium Dome? We will wait and see
And so we say hello to the millennium.

*Gary Harvey  (12)*
*Norton Hill School*


# Music Through The Years!

The best thing this century is expression through music.
The way that we play it, the way that we use it.
To annoy our parents and make a statement.
So they tell us to play it down in the basement.

They in turn had their rebellion,
With Elvis in the '50s.
Or if they were younger they listened to,
The Beatles in the 60s.

Then came the swinging 70s,
They were Bjorn again with ABBA.
Next there came the 80s,
Michael Jackson and the first rappers.

Finally the 90s
With Punk, Rock and Indie.
Greenday and Nirvana,
Amnesia and Peranih.

*Frankie Bray  (12)*
*Norton Hill School*


## LEAVING THE 20TH CENTURY

The swinging 60s were hippy times,
Then the coronation of the Queen was divine,
She wore posh clothes and make up too,
Then came the rise of the indoor loo,
Then antibiotics and drugs were taken,
And with all the earthquakes, the world was shaken,
The Beatles conquered the music charts,
Not forgetting the rest of the arts,
Elvis the king died,
The president Bill Clinton lied,
The space shuttle out in space,
Martin Luther King made us all the same race,
We are all worried about the greenhouse effect,
But with all this modern technology, what do we expect?
To this we have to say goodbye,
And let the 20th century and the millennium die!

*Abigail Bawden  (13)*
*Norton Hill School*

# MY MILLENNIUM WISH

It's goodbye to the 20th century
What will our future be
Can we match your great events
We'll just have to wait and see.

The world has been unsettled
Many deaths and senseless wars
People starving in a rich world
Where there are food mountain stores.

Men walking on the moon
Equal rights for women
Men taking *housewife* roles
In an upside down dizzy world.

Cures for most diseases
But new diseases found
Exceeding all speed records
In the air, the sea and on the ground.

Roaring 20s, Hippy 60s and Punk 70s
All music from pop to rock
Television to open up our tiny worlds
To inform and sometimes shock.

But what happens at 12 midnight
Will the technology let us down
And what about the Third World Debt
Can a solution be found?

No more starving people
No more senseless wars
Cures for all diseases
Is what we should be aiming for.

*Danielle Brooks (12)*
*Norton Hill School*

## GOODBYE TWENTIETH CENTURY

Twentieth century is the place to be.
It is the perfect place for me.
Things have happened through the years,
Like two World Wars,
And a few new laws,
Women got to vote,
And the Titanic wouldn't float.

The 60s crept upon us and flower power ruled
The computer was soon to follow,
Floppy discs and all.
Hang on to your satellite, they're
Talking about a crash
The millennium is just around the corner
It's going to be a big bash!

*Katie Fishlock  (12)*
*Norton Hill School*


## MILLENNIUM POEM

Millennium Dome built for a fact,
in case the world ends on impact,
it's got everything you need,
to keep you alive,
food, drink, water, air conditioning
or have you got anything else to bring.
You're not allowed out because it won't open
until a certain time,
but when it opens, you'll smell fresh air,
and then go to your house,
and feel happy about yourself.

*Michael Hayhoe  (12)*
*Norton Hill School*

## GOODBYE TO THE 20TH CENTURY

In the 20th century, the wars, the inventions,
the changes and the discoveries, in the 20th century . . .

In the 20th century there has been:
A film called The Titanic, that everyone has seen!

In the 20th century, women got the vote . . .
And everyone found out ABBA couldn't sing a note!

In the 20th century there were black rights,
After Nelson Mandela got in a fight!

In the 20th century there was the 60's flower power
But most of all, I will miss the Girl Power!

Bye, bye
20th century.

*Stephanie Postbechild  (12)*
*Norton Hill School*


## MILLENNIUM

Diana was the princess of the people's hearts,
when she died, it was a tragedy.
We must not remember this century
for sad times but happy ones and achievements.
We take things like the telephone and NHS for granted
these days but they were all invented this century.
We must all remember that everything was dreamt of.
So look forward to the future, don't live in the past,
only remember it.

*Kathryn Angwin  (12)*
*Norton Hill School*

# Good Times Never End (Ode To The 20th Century)

Tragedy of the Titanic liner, Charlie Chaplain in silent films.
World War One began and ended,
Alexander Fleming discovered penicillin,
Emmeline Pankhurst a devoted suffragette,
The first Tesco opened.

Harry George Ferguson invented the tractor,
World War Two began and ended.
Aneuris Bevan, NHS, Sir Winston Churchill was
Prime Minster in World War Two.
Sir Edmund Hillary up Mount Everest,
Queen's coronation on TV.

Roger Bannister ran a mile,
in the 60s, the Beatles ruled.
Neil Armstrong on the moon,
supersonic Concorde plane.
The Shuttle Columbia orbited Earth,
The Berlin Wall came crashing down.

Channel tunnel in '94, Nelson Mandela,
South Africa's president.
Computers are used for study, work and play,
the Spice Girls had girl power at their fingertips.

Party hard - 1999 - 2000!

*Natalie Kenrick  (12)*
*Norton Hill School*

# MY FRIEND KATIE!

She is my best friend,
And will be until the end.

Her name is Kate,
And at school she's never late.

She has long brown curly hair,
That's always flying through the air.

She is a couple of inches taller than me,
So I look up to her you see.

Her favourite subject is art,
And favourite pudding is tart.

She is very very funny,
And likes to spend her money.

She has a dog that's so mad,
That encourages all the lads.

She lives in North Road,
Her house keeps her warm in the cold.

Her hobbies are shopping and swimming too,
And after lunch she always needs the loo.

So that's my friend,
And will be until the end.

*Charlotte Hunter  (12)*
*Norton Hill School*

## 20TH CENTURY POEM

The TV, radio, the CD and computer,
were all invented in the 20th century.
The computer, the telephone, the video
and electrics
were all put into the houses.

Lots of amazing things have happened,
like walking on the moon,
lots of successes and achievements
were made,
like the car, the train and the aeroplane.

Lots of bad things have happened,
like the first and second World Wars.

*Amy Atkins (12)*
*Norton Hill School*


## MILLENNIUM POEM

The Millennium Dome is full of
Innovations and other things
I'm going to mention.
Like the innovation of flight
Which was a pure delight and
The first motor car which was quite bizarre.
There are also some bad things
That I'm going to
Say like the death of Princess Diana
On that terrible day.
The end of this millennium
We're all going to have a good time.
We'll also have a giant countdown.

*Lee Marks (12)*
*Norton Hill School*

## MILLENNIUM

The millennium is dawning
with a hangover the next morning,
with everyone partying away.

Norton will be rocking,
London will be shocking,
with the Queen dancing away.

Fireworks and disco,
drinking and fiasco
as the Millennium Dome is awake.

Everyone will be out that night,
definitely, without a doubt,
with drinking, partying and dreaming
as we all do the countdown.

5, 4, 3, 2, 1, a hug and a kiss from Mum,
the millennium is here,
there's no more to fear
as we all drink to the millennium.

*Alex Brain  (12)*
*Norton Hill School*


## 20TH CENTURY POEM

No more war planes flying,
No more soldiers dying,
The war has been forgotten,
Forgotten by the years.

Hitler has now gone,
Never again to bomb,
The war has been forgotten,
Forgotten by the years.

Now the countries are at peace,
All the captives long released,
The war has been forgotten,
Forgotten by the years.

The blood once spilt has dried,
So have tears once cried!
The war has been forgotten,
Forgotten by the years.

*Hayley Cribb  (11)*
*Norton Hill School*


## MILLENNIUM

We all ask ourselves what is the millennium?
But no one knows what it is for sure.
Everyone is talking about it,
And we're all very excited,
About this special New Year's Eve.

The Dome is growing,
And parties are brewing
Everyone is having a buzz!
But no one is sure what
It holds in store.

Maybe new computers
Prepare new bright colour toasters
New clothes, new shoes
But no one knows for sure.

It's going to be a surprise
Of dazzling lights and lots of noise
Because this is a turn in the century.

*Jennifer Tapper  (12)*
*Norton Hill School*

## THE TWENTIETH CENTURY

The twentieth century has almost gone,
I can't believe it, we have had two great wars
The first and the second and the atomic bomb
Was used when necessary.

The computer was invented along with the phone
And also the TV, oh yes the love of my life
In which I couldn't live without.

I look back to the flower power,
Hippies and camper vans.
The psychedelic age must have been great
With beautiful colours everywhere.

Later to date the death of Diana, a tragic loss to everyone.
Millions flocked from all over the world to see her
Dead body escorted to her grave, one of the many
Memories that we cannot forget.

Over the years our technology has advanced
Soon there will be robots and life form other than ours
Things are going too far, pollution from cars
Slowly breaking down our ozone layer.
*Why can't it all just stop?*

*Dan Redgewell (12)*
*Norton Hill School*

# GOODBYE TO ALL THAT

Goodbye to all the Beatles; George, Ringo, Paul and John
Goodbye Abba and Elvis, now that you have gone
Goodbye to all the popstars, your journey has been long
But we will still remember your very greatest song.

Goodbye to all inventions the lap top and PC
Goodbye to all computers and even the TV
Goodbye to the radiator and the telephone
But we still make inventions even on our own.

Hello to the year 2000 is coming right at you
Hello to new ideas that come from out of the blue
The world is changing quickly and new ideas are born
What comes next we wonder, happy or forlorn?

*Kate Lawrence (11)*
*Norton Hill School*


# THE MILLENNIUM

The millennium -
one thousand years of progress
inventions galore.

M edicine marvels over the years
I  nventions created by man
L  uxury is for the rich
L  eisure is for comfort
E  xploration took us to the moon
N  ew year, we have seen a few
N  uclear weapons destroyed our peace
I  ntelligence gave us windows 98
U  niverse where it all began
M oon where we might live.

*Aaron Welch (12)*
*Norton Hill School*

## MILLENNIUM

The millennium is nearly here,
But as I peer
Back in time
I make this rhyme.

The books say
Hitler had to pay
For treating England that way
We killed them all
And Britain stood tall
The Americans finished it
When the nuclear bomb in Japan hit.

As I look towards today
I can proudly say
England won the World Cup in '66
Three years after we walked the moon
Humans might live there soon.

As a computer era is here
They might rule next year
But we can shut them down
That'll make them frown
What will happen in a year?
At the moment it isn't clear.

*Jacob Ingram  (11)*
*Norton Hill School*

# MILLENNIUM

Last two days of 1999,
The end is here but that's just fine,
Leaving behind a century of disaster,
The hours go by faster and faster,
To start this poem I think I'll write,
About the wars and years of fight,
Thousands of men dressed in green,
Wander into danger unseen,
Children cried upon their beds,
Crying over, parents dead.

But now we're back to happier times,
So forget the war, the dirt, the grime,
The millennium is nearly here,
So there's no need to fear.

On the moon the first man stood,
Whilst down below they hoped he could,
JFK shot in his prime,
Who really did commit this crime?

Elvis Presley they called him the king,
Because he was a man who could really sing,
Bootleg trousers and lots of flares,
Platform shoes and crazy hair!

Now the millennium is here to stay,
Life will be fun in every way!

*Jessica Colbourne  (11)*
*Norton Hill School*

## A WALK ALONG THE WAY

Walking along the river bank,
a distance of a way.
Birds flying overhead,
on a summer's day.

The sun shines brightly,
the clouds are white.
Blue sky all around,
what a lovely sight.

The boats travel up the stream,
passing by each other,
Gliding slowly through the water,
Look - here comes another.

Children playing close nearby,
having lots of fun.
They sit eating ice-cream,
melted by the sun.

And as I walked along the way,
I started to remember
of all the fun that's around,
when it's snowing in December.

*Hannah Yeates  (15)*
*Norton Hill School*

## GOODBYE 20TH CENTURY

Goodbye,

G reat films,
O deon Cinemas opened,
O ld Titanic sunk,
D iana died,
B eatles break through,
Y early fashions,
E clipse watched by millions of people.

T V was invented,
O ne man on the Moon with his friends.

T he radio was invented,
H umans sent into space,
E ngines used a lot.

C ars invented,
E nglish sent to war,
N ASA sent first rocket into space,
T ransport became easier,
U SA sent to war,
R oald Dahl wrote some brilliant children's novels.
Y ou were born.

*Ben Parker (12)*
*Norton Hill School*

# MILLENNIUM

A poem about the 20th century using the total alphabet, it goes from 1900 up to 2000 putting only important things in, so here we go. Let's start with A . . .

A is for Aeroplanes, the things which let us fly.
B is for Better, an education at school.
C is for Computers, you play as time passes by.
D is for Diana's death, a big tragedy.
E is for Electricity, where would we be without it?
F is for First, the man on the moon.
G is for Global Warming, a hole in the ozone layer.
H is for Harry, a Royal Prince.
I is for Inventions, we've had plenty of them.
J is for Jaguar, an expensive car.
K is for Kings, we've had many of them.
L is for Lorries, large vehicles.
M is for Millennium, the Dome has been built.
N is for New, a century is starting.
O is for Operations, the hospitals carry out.
P is for Packet, the new sweets.
Q is for Queen, as one is on the throne.
R is for Rides, they're new at the fair.
S is for Sophie, her marriage to Edward.
T is for Technology, better tools.
U is for University, a clever school.
V is for Vodaphone, a mobile phone company.
W is for Warm, a happy century.
X is for Xylophone, a musical instrument.
Y is for You, living your own life.
Z is for Zebra Crossing, it helps you cross the roads.

So there you have it, the century has come to an end, so let's go and celebrate the new millennium. Put your party hats on, and get your wine glasses out, relax and enjoy yourself until the millennium is out.

*Felicity Vine  (12)*
*Norton Hill School*


## FAREWELL TO THE 20TH CENTURY

Goodbye 20th century,
Hello the 21st.
We leave behind,
Some great events,
Like when cloning
Made Dolly the sheep.
And mankind made a gigantic leap,
By walking on the moon.

A king resigns a princess dies,
And all the land is stunned.
Great politicians rise and fall,
Like Winston Churchill hero of the war.
And Margaret Thatcher the first woman to be
Leader of our own country.

Inventions too, have made their mark,
Planes fly us round the world.
Computers, TV, mobile phones,
CDs, tapes as well.
Without all these how would we cope?
In our modern world.

*Helen Warne  (12)*
*Norton Hill School*

## BRITAIN AT WAR

B ritain's at war,
R adio announcing we are at war,
I nto air raid shelters quickly,
T he Germans are bombing,
A fter Hitler had left us for one more day
I n the afternoon we see if our homes are still there,
N early everyone crying.

A fter we have come out of the shelter,
T owns are destroyed,

W e soon hope war is over,
A policeman says the war's off,
R eturn evacuees, the war is over!

*Melanie Brent  (12)*
*Norton Hill School*

## MILLENNIUM

M ost people will be celebrating its end.
I have lived for only 12 of its years.
L ots of changes have happened during it.
L asers have become widely used.
E cology has become a big issue through it.
N ASA sent men to the moon.
N ew technology is being invented all the time.
I will be part of it.
U niverse has been explored more and more.
*M illennium.*

*Richard Curtis  (12)*
*Norton Hill School*

## 100 YEARS

Over the last 100 years
many things have changed.
We have gone from steam to
electric with the train.

We have landed on the moon,
and flown in balloons.

Cars have stopped and started,
TVs, music and videos can now
be recorded.

Lasers and computer chips
are great things,
we use them in almost everything.

Paper and plastic, silk and vinyl,
these are all things that help
our survival.

*Emma Dall  (13)*
*Norton Hill School*


## CENTURY

C is for central powers in the world war,
E is for Edward VII, died in 1910.
N is for Nicholas II, died in 1918.
T is for Thatcher, Margaret, the first woman to be Prime Minister.
U is for Universal Declaration of Human Rights.
R is for rap music.
Y is for Yom Kippur War.

*Lisa Wheeler  (12)*
*Norton Hill School*

## GOODBYE TWENTIETH CENTURY

This thousand years have nearly passed,
To older people, it's gone real fast!
Many things have come and gone,
Two World Wars and a nuclear bomb.

Then came in football the World Cup,
In '66 we had good luck.
A hat-trick was scored by our Geoff Hurst,
While German spectators booed and cursed.

The Americans took off in space,
And beat the Russians in the race.
Nothing on the planet did they find,
But Neil Armstrong made a leap for mankind.

But here I am, thirteen years old,
What does the new millennium hold?
Wars and disasters I hope won't last,
I hope they're just a thing of the past.

*Becca Clarke  (13)*
*Norton Hill School*


## MILLENNIUM!

Millennium is now here,
we've had a very good year, 1999,
but we've had one thousand years.
We wanted to drink beer
to celebrate the time,
but how am I to celebrate
without staying up too late?
People were having a good time.
Millennium!

*Luke Collins  (12)*
*Norton Hill School*

# 20TH CENTURY

England won the football world cup,
back in 1966.
A man set foot on the face of the moon,
an adventure for all to follow.
Then World War One began, thought to
be the last, but twenty years later, it started
over again.
Aircraft technology, by then was so advanced,
a better, faster machine was made,
now known as Concorde.
Yet again, another masterpiece,
the unsinkable Titanic,
shown to be incorrect when in 1912,
her first voyage, she hit an iceberg and fell to her ocean bed.
But now in 1999, the millennium ahead,
we look forward to the future,
the achievements waiting to be had.

*Matthew Harle (12)*
*Norton Hill School*


## LAST CHANCE

The darkness coming closer,
Edging nearer,
Will it be the end?
The countdown has begun,
Like the black smoke choking the world,
From Marilyn Monroe to Madonna,
All memories will fade,
The whole world forgotten,
Towards a new beginning,
Goodbye to the 20th century.

*Frances Mullins (11)*
*Norton Hill School*

# A CENTURY OF TIME

Turn back the clocks one hundred years,
Think of the fear, happiness and tears,
Victorian times had come to an end,
The Edwardian reign set a new trend.

1903 saw the world's first powered flight,
Took off from North Carolina with the brothers Wright,
1914 was the First World War,
Thousands of people died, maybe more.

1926 was important when doing my revision,
I discovered John Logie Baird invented television,
1939 and Europe raged with war,
Hitler invaded Poland by taking the back door.

Victory bells at last started loudly ringing,
Hopefully 1945 was a new beginning,
Technology and science moves forward with pace,
Discoveries in medicine save the human race.

1960s saw a great revolution,
Scan the world's aware of its pollution,
Fashion and pop music are on the way up,
England beats Germany to win the World Cup.

On the moon the Eagle landed,
Neil Armstrong took a step single handed,
The great leap for mankind,
Something that will stick deeply in my mind.

Conservatives everywhere celebrated when
Margaret Thatcher took over at number ten,
The first female leader to be elected,
She grew in stature and was respected.

The Falklands' war brewed in the south seas,
The Berlin Wall suddenly crashes to its knees,
Haunting memories in my mind,
Was the death of Diana, princess kind?

Now here we are at the present day,
What's in the future, who can say?

*Melissa Kendall  (13)*
*Norton Hill School*


## GOODBYE TO THE TWENTIETH CENTURY

Neil Armstrong made it to the moon,
One August day total eclipse,
The swinging 60s flower power time,
The Beatles, ABBA hit the music charts.
England and Germany went to war,
The Brits came home heroes.
Man United won the treble,
1966 England won the World Cup,
Mother Theresa passed away,
Princess Diana tragically died,
Goodbye to the twentieth century.

Nelson Mandella the first black president,
The Berlin wall came down,
Margaret Thatcher first woman Prime Minister,
J F Kennedy shot in the head,
The Titanic sunk at sea,
Royal yacht Britannia retired,
Goodbye to the twentieth century.

*Ben Chard  (12)*
*Norton Hill School*

## YEAR 2000 POEM

The 20th century is coming to a close,
A time of great inventions,
Including television and radios.

A time in which there were two world wars,
And smaller ones as well,
Also other tragedies including Princess Di.

Goodbye to the 20th century,
The one in which I was born,
Here's to the next millennium,
Cheers to you all.

*Alan Miles (12)*
*Norton Hill School*


## TWO THOUSAND

T welve months to date from January to December.
W e will be leaving behind a wonderful millennium.
O n to the year 2000 we go.

T he millennium will be gone.
H ello year 2000
O ur parties will be starting
U seless to look back
S tart to look forward
A re you ready?
N o more 1999
D eparting from this millennium we go.

*Adam Martin (12)*
*Norton Hill School*

## THE ECLIPSE

It was the 11th of August,
The sun was high in the sky,
People from everywhere gathered,
They gathered and gazed at the sky.

Some people gathered on Land's End in Cornwall,
Some gathered in Jersey,
Some people gathered in Concorde
And followed the moon's journey.

Some people in Japan were frightened,
Frightened of the dragon,
The dragon that they believed was eating the sun,
They made noises to scare the dragon.

Suddenly the Earth was quiet,
Everyone put on their glasses and looked into the sky,
The quiet only lasted for a while,
Now the Earth's noisy, busy as normal.

*Kayleigh Lewis  (12)*
*Norton Hill School*


## THE TITANIC

The strong ship started to sink,
It hit an iceberg on that cold April night,
The ship was called Titanic,
People thought she wouldn't sink,
At twenty to two in the morning,
The Atlantic swallowed her up,
Now in the Atlantic she lies,
In the cold dark blue sea
The strong ship is no more.

*Michaela Beale  (12)*
*Norton Hill School*

# MILLENNIUM

The century started with deaths and many tears,
Two world wars in thirty years.
Hitler was the evil one who killed all the Jews,
But Churchill fought back and made the Nazis old news.

The atom bomb and the Ford model T,
Are just a few of the inventions in this century.
USA, Japan and Russia,
Emerge as the greatest with all the power.

In '46, the first computer was built,
The troubles began with many people killed.
AIDs was diagnosed for the very first time,
Armstrong reached the moon in '69.

NASA launched the Hubbel space telescope,
In Germany at last there's a bit of hope.
Nelson Mandela becomes the first black leader,
This makes the natives a lot happier.

But now it's 1999, the millennium's nearly passed
What have we learnt from this century, it's gone really fast.

*James Clark  (14)*
*Norton Hill School*


# THE ECLIPSE

It was 1999,
And the sun was high in the sky,
We saw a black shadow,
And knew it was the eclipse.

We put our glasses on,
And looked at the sun,
The shadow we saw,
As it covered the sun.

It went all black,
And after a couple of minutes,
It uncovered the sun,
And we saw the sun again.

We took off our glasses,
Went inside,
And talked about what we had seen,
And knew we had seen an eclipse.

*Jade Corp  (13)*
*Norton Hill School*


## HOPE

An evil darkness spreads across the Earth,
Death, pain, destruction, grief, we're torn.
Mankind's lost generation of no worth,
But in the morning we'll remember them as we mourn.

Gas masks, mess tins, letters from home, five Woodbines,
Land girls toil then rest in clover,
Soldiers bloodied but proud clutching a carbine,
Together they walk along the white cliffs of Dover.

Peace, rock and roll, a flower in your hair,
The dawn of a new age.
A giant leap for mankind, space doesn't care,
Martin and John, civil rights out of Vietnam.
Turning of a page?

This world is full of pollution,
In our land, sea and air,
People of the world unite, there must be a solution
For peace and harmony all living creatures need to share.

*Peri Harris  (14)*
*Norton Hill School*

## MY NEW SCHOOL

I've learnt to like my school,
It has a certain special rule,
Don't graffiti on your book,
Or you'll get that funny look.
I like my teachers very much,
You have to be good such such so much,
Or you'll get the dreaded word
*Detention!* Missing your lunch with lemon curd.
You will get your locker by a week
You may have to play a game of hide and seek.
Sometimes your locker cannot be found,
Others make a horrible squeaky sound.
Some teachers are kind,
Others just can't make up their mind.
Some teachers have a funny name,
Others are just rather plain.
Now you see that my school
Has a certain special rule,
Of course it does have more,
But they might be a bit of a bore.

*Louise Hole  (11)*
*Norton Hill School*


## THE DESERT WAR

As everyone scrambled into their Grants,
They were all flanked,
They fired their shells,
And blew the enemy to hell.

They got out of the base,
They were heading to open space,
They were being chased,
At an incredible pace.

They got to a ridge,
With a bridge going across it,
They went across it single file,
Turned round, fired and made a pile of rubble.

One of the men radioed for help,
While undoing his belt,
It was very hot,
All of a sudden there was a shot.

*Russell Gould  (12)*
*Norton Hill School*


## GOODBYE TWENTIETH CENTURY

Twentieth century man stepped on the moon
Twentieth century World War I-II
Twentieth century cinema came to town
Twentieth century different kind of transport
England win World Cup in '66
Computers invented, Internet access, new medicines
1912 Titanic sinks
Diana Princess of Wales dies in car crash
CDs invented
Music such as
ABBA
Beatles
Elvis
Spice Girls
All big hits
Star Wars all four of them
Twentieth Century I'll miss you

Twenty-first century I just can't wait for it.

*Daniel Rogers  (11)*
*Norton Hill School*

## ALL IN A SINGLE NIGHT

On Hallowe'en
I'm sure you've seen
That's when evil spirits come out.
Yes they come out,
Playing about,
On the empty street.

First of all they raid the shores,
Then, of course, they cover doors
With eggs and flour and stuff.
But, sadly, this isn't enough.

You are in your house
You think you're safe.
But the ghosts and ghouls are tough,
For in your house they can appear,
In just, a single puff.

Someone knocks at the door,
Round the door you peer,
Then suddenly you hear
'Trick or treat?'

You go to the kitchen and take a seat,
Think what to give them nice to eat,
You look around until you spot
A Milk Tray box
Full of chocs.
You go to the door and say 'Boo!'
For all the chocs are inside you.

*Michelle Bohan  (14)*
*Norton Hill School*

## THE FIRST MAN ON THE MOON

He climbed into the capsule
As quiet as could be,
He was really nervous
He was sweating in his white suit,
His helmet misted up
As it was a very cold day,
He sat down and belted up
As the rest sorted out the food,
He was ready to take off
They closed the capsule door,
Five, four, three, two, one
*Blast off*
He was off to the moon
As the steam coming out
As the rocket blasts off,
He was finally there
Far away from Earth,
Looking at the round ball that shines,
The bubbly moon
Felt like cheese,
The hard, bumpy moon
White was all you could see,
The moon went on
The green people startled me,
As they walked around
With their little laser guns,
Their little houses
Looked like igloos
He had enough for one day,
And returned home
On the only rocket
That had ever been to the moon.

*Sophie Louise McCarthy (12)*
*Norton Hill School*

## Goodbye 20th Century

An empire mourns Queen Victoria.
A noble prize for Dr Curie.
A grand flight by the brothers Wright.
South Pole race lost by Brits.
The unsinkable sinks.
A generation is lost in the war to end wars.
A sneeze brings universal cure.
A man named Hitler starts hell on Earth.
Six million Jews paid the price.
It only ends with a bomb.
USA worries about Reds.
Queen Elizabeth crowned
And Stalin dead.
The four minute mile is finally broken.
A man named Haley shows us how to rock.
'I have a dream' says Luther King.
JFK dies.
Armstrong takes one small step.
100,000 women march for their rights.
First test tube baby takes a breath.
Chernobyl releases a deadly cloud.
People take one last look at the Berlin wall.
Nelson Mandela at last goes home.
A saintly nun loses her fight,
But even so our future's bright.

*Cally Lane  (12)*
*Norton Hill School*

## TIME FOR A CHANGE

T here's been lots of changes in the last century
I f there hadn't there'd be lots of difficulties
M ore and more our lives have changed
E ndless inventions there's been more and more

F rom a horse-drawn carriage to a motorised car
O r other sorts of transport like aeroplanes and trains
R ockets launching into space

A rmstrong first set foot on the moon

C oncorde can take you to the USA, and
H ome again in less than a day
A eroplanes can take us far away
N ow we are looking forward to the millennium
G oing into a new century
E ven more things to explore and find.

*Lauren Trippick  (13)*
*Norton Hill School*


## THE ECLIPSE

When the eclipse first started in 1999,
I thought it was amazing,
About halfway through the eclipse
I went outside and it was getting dark,
I know you weren't meant to
But I looked up to the eclipse very quickly,
My eyes were OK,
Then suddenly the eclipse had finished,
Then a big light came round the moon,
It was amazing.

*Alex Price  (12)*
*Norton Hill School*

## GOODBYE TO ALL THAT

Why is this poem saying goodbye,
To the history we have known for so long,
The things that have happened,
Cannot be erased from our memories.
Just because the date has changed,
The year 2000 does not mean we never won the World Cup,
Or that we won't remember the tragic death of Diana,
That we can't commiserate those deaths in the Falklands,
Or not wear the poppies of the bloody Flanders field,
When the first year of 2000 has gone,
Will that be the only history we can have?
We should remember the history whether with pride, joy or pain,
So let's not say goodbye to this century that's gone,
But remember it as we say hello to the one to come.

*Kirsty Diclaudio  (13)*
*Norton Hill School*


## 20TH CENTURY

We have invented things for the good of man
But then exploited them as we can,
Like the nuclear devices that we build,
We then abuse them for the battlefield.
Of all our great inventions,
Which of them had bad intentions?
There have been advances in medical science
But what about an end to violence?
We have great things like the Internet
And brill toys eg Cyber pets.
But all inventions, even flight
Are all about man's 'great might'.

*James Bona  (13)*
*Norton Hill School*

## THE BRISTOL BLITZ

England was at war,
The city of Bristol was in danger,
Britain was in danger,
To hear Churchill's voice was bad news.

Bombs falling all around us,
Like yesterday bombs fall all night long,
Lighting the sky like flashing torches flashing.

People ran into their bomb shelters,
So many families destroyed,
The children were evacuated from their homes.

Hundreds of people killed,
Hitler killed our families,
Oh Hitler go away!
The Bristol Blitz was the worst ever.

*Alison Gillard (12)*
*Norton Hill School*

## MAN ON THE MOON

Step out of the ship,
On to the moon,
Put a flag in the ground,
Collect some moon rock,
Put it in the shuttle,
Start up the engines,
Away we go back to Earth.

*Sam Pratten (12)*
*Norton Hill School*

## GOODBYE TO ALL THAT

The millennium,
Look it up in a dictionary and it will simply say;
A thousand years.
As if that's all it is,
A thousand years.
No mention of World War One,
Or World War Two,
Like it's unimportant, it's just
A thousand years.
In this time,
The first plane flew,
The first car was driven,
The radio was invented,
And later, the TV was brought to life,
But did any of that matter?
No. According to the dictionary, it's still,
A thousand years.
The Battle of Hastings was fought,
Women were given equal rights,
Abraham Lincoln abolished slavery in America,
The Berlin wall came down,
I could go on and on and on,
But if you look under millennium in the dictionary,
It still doesn't mention any of those things,
It's irrelevant, it simply states,
A thousand years.
We discovered gravity,
And much later, the first man was on the moon,
Computers, CDs, videos, camcorders,
They were all invented too,
But, the dictionary remains too stubborn to compromise,
And just mention a few of these things,

So now as we say goodbye to all of that,
And we enter the next millennium,
We cross our fingers and hope that next time
The dictionary gets it right,
And comes to terms with the fact,
That a millennium is not, just:
A thousand years!

*Hannah Jones  (13)*
*Norton Hill School*


## THE ECLIPSE

When I got up the sun was shining
I was outside when it got cloudy and cold.
I came in and watched television.
This is the eclipse I was told.

It was dark and creepy in my room.
When the sun slowly covered the moon.
It all happened up in the sky.
It was a wonderful sight I can't describe it.

In Penzance it was darker.
Streetlights came on.
People stood all around.
Waiting to see something new from the ground.

Hooray it was here.
The diamond ring bright like magnesium white.
This was very real.
It was very quiet and still.

The sun slowly appeared again.
So I could go outside and play.
This had been a special day.

*Jemma Taylor  (11)*
*Norton Hill School*

## GOODBYE TO THE 20TH CENTURY

Some things I know about,
But a lot of things I don't,
But one of the things I do know
Is it has been a great century.

Over the last hundred years,
There have been good things
And there have been bad
But overall it's been a great century.

In '66 we won the World Cup,
In 1912 the Titanic sank
In '39 there was a world war
But overall it's been a great century.

*Todd Lane  (11)*
*Norton Hill School*


## GOODBYE 20TH CENTURY

Twentieth century had World War I and II come.
Man lands on the moon.
Man makes computers.
England host the World Cup and win it in 1966.
1912 has death of lots of people on the Titanic.
Air travel with aeroplanes are fastest passenger plane the Concorde.
Diana dies in crash and Jill Dando murdered.
Pop and rock singers Elvis, Abba and Beatles.
America loses most of the most famous family, the Kennedys.
So if all this happened in the 20th century
I want to go into the 21st century.

*Andrew Withers  (11)*
*Norton Hill School*

## GOODBYE 20TH CENTURY

Farewell 20th Century,
It's sad to see you go.
Aeroplanes were invented and computers too,
But then there were the bad things, such as
World War II, and Princess Diana died.
But I like to remember the good things,
Like when we won the World Cup.
Then again, when the 20th century was bad
It was very, very bad,
Like when Titanic sank,
But also there was girl power . . .
*Nah!*
*Goodbye!*

*Tom Williams  (11)*
*Norton Hill School*


## GOODBYE TO THE 20TH CENTURY

Goodbye to the 20th century
Nothing much happened then,
Except for the invention of computers
And maybe girl power too,
And when microwaves started cooking
And satellites went to Mars,
And when England won the World Cup
And people made car telephones,
And toilets, thank God
I s'pose it wasn't that bad after all
But if you think the 20th century was good,
. . . Wait until the 21st!

*Laura Smith  (11)*
*Norton Hill School*

## GOODBYE TWENTIETH CENTURY

Goodbye twentieth century,
For Titanic and her glory,
For Hitler,
And World War II,
For aeroplanes, Concorde,
And the Vietnam war.
Goodbye twentieth century
For the population of mankind,
For the death of Princess Diana
And Jill Dando,
For Neil Armstrong on the moon,
And bands like ABBA, Beatles,
And the king of rock Elvis.
Goodbye twentieth century,
For Spice Girls and girl power,
For enjoyments like television,
Cinemas and PlayStations,
For telephones,
And women in trousers,
Goodbye twentieth century . . .
We will miss you.

*Jen Welfare  (12)*
*Norton Hill School*


## MY DOG

M orris is so funny and so silly
O f course you can't tell him off
R eason being we love him so much
R ather greedy
I t is not a problem to me
S o Morris is the best, I love him loads.

*Harriet Gordon  (11)*
*Oldfield School*

## TROPICAL ISLAND

All alone on a colourful tropical island,
Ground wind makes boiling hot sand
Blow and sting my ankles.

A scarlet and sky-blue parrot
Flies from the feathery leaves
Of a bright flamboyant tree.

The clear gentle blue of the ocean's waves
Is calming and relaxing.
Fresh, pure and natural smells
Of succulent fruits and leafy trees.

Suddenly the wind rises up,
Overhead stormy clouds dropping out,
Turning the island upside down.

After a minute it's gone.
The sun appears, shining from behind the haze
All is calm and tranquil once more.

*Leanne Burgess  (11)*
*Oldfield School*


## IS THAT GIRL IN THE SNAPSHOT ME?

'Is that girl in the snapshot me?'
With the cute little smile.
Is that the girl that ran round the house,
Then fell asleep with her small white teddy?
Is that the girl with her mother's eyes,
And her father's knees?
'Is that girl in the snapshot me?'

*Alice Palfrey  (11)*
*Oldfield School*

# MY LIFE

On October the 21st,
The date that I was born,
I was lying there so happy,
On the cold winter morn.

Then just before my sister was born,
I thought I would be helpful,
I went out to collect the milk,
And dropped it, making trouble.

Next came my sister's birth,
But I can't remember much,
The only thing I can remember,
Was seeing her in a clear like hutch.

Before I knew it I was starting school,
A big girl I would be now,
Wearing a uniform that big people wore,
So amazing, I loved it, wow!

Now I've just started at Oldfield,
I find it really great and fun,
Next week I will be twelve years old,
But everybody says that my life's just begun.

In the future I hope to be a vet,
With two ponies as well,
I'm going to own a cottage
In the country, won't that be swell?

*Clare Pearce  (11)*
*Oldfield School*

## IS THAT GIRL IN THE SNAPSHOT ME?

Is that girl in the snapshot me?
The one standing by the Christmas tree?
The one with the light golden hair?
The one wearing the really long skirt?

I don't remember much about that day -
Only what my family say.
I remember the place - my old flat
I remember my age - six or more.

I remember that it was my dad's idea
To dress us up really queer
But even despite my unhappy face
One thing's for sure - we had a happy day.

*Rachel Sleeper (11)*
*Oldfield School*


## THE RAINMAKER

He was tall, thin and elegant
His eyes were deep within the clouds
The blues which changed to emerald greens
Made him stand out from the crowds.

His clothes so ragged and tattered
The buttons falling from the thread
The collar stood up rigid
And from his eyes, tears of rain they shed.

And yet these tears so freely spilt
Brought happiness to all below
For they brought life back to the Earth,
And caused the countryside to grow.

*Jessie Seckington (11)*
*Oldfield School*

# ROSES' CARAMEL KEGS!

I was once a young little thing,
who used to scream and sing,
while lying on my back kicking my legs,
eating Roses' caramel kegs,
which melt in the mouth
though they're bad for your health,
I love to eat them,
nothing can beat them.

Now I'm older,
my singing's much bolder,
*But,*
I still lie on my back and kick my legs,
while eating Roses' caramel kegs,
which melt in the mouth,
though they're bad for your health,
I love to eat them,
nothing can beat them.

*I loveRoses' caramel kegs!*

**Louise Mitcheson  (11)**
**Oldfield School**


# PUPPY POEM

I'm getting a puppy,
A bundle of fun.
I can't wait to tell everyone.
They're sweet and cuddly, friendly too,
They like to play around with you.
If you are bored, have nothing to do,
Puppies are the ideal pet for you.

**Laura Heselgrove  (11)**
**Oldfield School**

## PLEASE NO MORE...

Please no more I'll be sick,
Honest,
Oh, that cake looks so lonely,
I'd better eat it so that it's not on its own.

Now I will be sick,
Honest,
That smells so good what is it?
A bacon buttie you say?
Oh well, I better eat it.

No more, please I'll be sick!
Honest,
What's for afters?
Ice-cream with sauce and wafers you say?
Oh, I love ice-cream.

Right that's it I've got to stop,
What's that?
My brother's been to the sweet shop. *Sweet* shop?
I get hooked on sweets, *mmm* tasty.

Mum I'm going to be sick,
Whoops too late,
Oh sorry,
Mum look at the dog!

*Sophie Allen  & Isabel Smetek  (13)*
*Oldfield School*

## SECONDARY SCHOOL

Butterflies swarmed round my belly,
My legs were wobbling like jelly.

Is secondary school as good as it sounds?
What if I get lost and go out of bounds?

What if the teacher gives me a detention?
My sister says it's something you don't want to mention!

Where am I? What am I doing here?
Why am I standing here trembling with fear?

I wiped the tears out of my eye,
what good would it do if I started to cry?

As I stared round the room I noticed I wasn't alone.

There were girls everywhere wearing white cotton shirts,
and blue trousers or knee-length skirts.

Where is my best friend?
The one who would stay by my side until it was the end.

I made a friend she was OK,
but I have to admit she brightened up my day!

*Emily Bradley (11)*
*Oldfield School*


## OUR BUDGIE

Our budgie is called Zippy,
He acts a bit like a hippy,
Hopping all around the cage,
Looking like he's in a rage,
He's had enough, he's fallen asleep,
In a funny big blue heap.

Morning comes and breakfast's here,
Suddenly Zippy gives a cheer,
In his cage we put some toast,
That's the thing that he loves most,
Singing and chirping all the day,
If only he'd come out to play.

*Kellie Butterton  (11)*
*Oldfield School*


## HAPPINESS

Happiness cries out for joy,
It sounds like the song of a baby bird.
Listen to it inside your heart,
It's the most wonderful thing that can be heard.

Happiness spreads a smile on your face,
As it smells as fresh as a tender red rose.
Smell it and smile for the queen of the flowers,
And float away as the gentle breeze blows.

Happiness sees right through the darkness,
It looks like the wind travelling from place to place,
See it in the deepest part of your eyes,
Where a smile appears and spreads over your face.

Happiness takes the hunger away,
It tastes like sweet honey on buttered bread,
Taste it - sweet and wonderful,
A smile escapes from inside your head.

Happiness pushes the coldness away,
It feels like the warmth from deep inside,
Touch it from deep down in your heart,
And let happiness be with you, by your side.

*Michelle Osborne  (11)*
*Oldfield School*

# IS THAT GIRL IN THE SNAPSHOT ME?

Is that girl in the snapshot me?
With long wavy hair and chubby cheeks?
Are you sure it's me and not my sister,
Or maybe even my cousin?
I can't imagine me wearing that dress,
With a pink frilly shell-like hem,
I can't imagine me wearing those shoes,
Black and shiny with buckles!
I remember who took the picture,
It was Dad I think.
I can remember the ice-blue wallpaper.
It doesn't look like me Mum!
Are you sure it's me Mum?
Are you sure?

*Faye Scarrott  (11)*
*Oldfield School*


# AM I IN THIS PICTURE?

What I want to know,
Is that where I used to go?
In a little pink dress
I looked pretty, I guess
What I really wanted to know,
Did I have fair hair as it will show?
I think I have changed a bit
I'm glad I don't wear a silly bib
I can't remember climbing out of my cot
I think I have changed an awful lot.

*Kirsty Hiles  (11)*
*Oldfield School*

## FUNFAIR

The funfair glows with excitement and joy.
It roars with the crazy screams, giggles
And lively chatter.
A sizzling smoky smell lingers about the heated air.
My mouth feels dry and stale.
All around me, bright lights flash their many different colours.
I love it here, I'm having so much fun!
Here comes Dad now, with our hot dogs, to join us in the queue
For the Ferris wheel.
Groups of hysterical teenagers rumble past us
Making their way to the crazy dare-devil rides,
Eager to prove how brave they are.
I can feel a strange buzz of excitement.
It's getting late now, and the darkness creeps in
With a nipping chill tagging along behind.
I have had loads of candyfloss and two toffee apples,
I'm feeling a little queasy.
The booming songs and hectic sounds never end,
I'm beginning to get a headache . . .
I still love it though!
Suddenly I hear a loud *bang* and stare up heavenwards
Fireworks crackle and explode, lighting up the night sky.
It looks absolutely amazing!
Perfect for rounding off the evening.
Well, it's time to go home now (straight to bed)!
I've had a brilliant time. Here's to next year!

*Lucy Bence-Wilkins*
*Oldfield School*

## AUTUMN

The leaves float from the trees,
Golden yellow,
Bronzy red,
Browny orange,
But still a touch of green,
Walking up the garden path,
Kicking the leaves away from my shoes,
Thinking what I would do,
If I could touch the cloudy sky,
Float away on a cloud,
Up about the trees,
Watch the autumn pass away,
Watch the leaves fade,
Slowly,
Steadily,
Now they're gone,
Come back down it's winter now,
With not a sound to be heard,
Not even the chirp of a little bird,
Soon it starts to snow,
So I go back in to warm my toes,
But I will be back out to make a snowman.

*Danielle Churm  (11)*
*Oldfield School*


## THE GARDEN IS A SIGHT TO BE SEEN

The leaves on the trees,      .
Are blowing softly in the breeze,
What a sight in summer,
All lush and green,
The garden is a sight to be seen.

In autumn are brown and reds,
They fall upon the flowers beds,
Soon brown and crinkly,
They will be found,
Thickly scattered on the ground.

*Chloe Hamlin  (11)*
*Oldfield School*


## POEMS!

I want to write a poem
One that doesn't rhyme
One that makes no sense
And doesn't keep in time.

I'll make my poem come to life
I'll make it scream and shout!
The only problem is . . .
I don't know what to write about.

I could write about bats
And cats
And rats
I could write about sharks
And singing larks
With tall pink flamingos
And big white rhinos.

But I don't think I'm doing very well
I think this poem rhymes
I know that it makes sense
And it does keep in time!

*Carrie Davies*
*Oldfield School*

## MY DREAM

My dream is to own an island,
Big tropical fruits,
Large colourful parrots,
Luscious coconut trees,
And a wooden house, built by my own hands.

My dream is to own an island,
Clear, cool, blue sea,
Dolphins leaping out of the water,
Soft, white sand,
And a tree house built by my own hands.

My dream is to own an island,
Monkeys swinging from tree to tree,
Sparkling, silver streams,
Blue and pink shells and corals,
And a boat built by my own hands.

*Rosanna Footitt (11)*
*Oldfield School*


## DIFFERENT

Everyone is different, special and unique,
It might be that we have different coloured hair, eyes, skin
We might believe different things
But think how the world would be
If we were all the same
It would be boring and dim and
You would share the same feelings
As millions of others
Respect each other share and remember
At heart everyone wants the same peace and happiness.

*Katie Naish (12)*
*Oldfield School*

## SEASONS

S pring comes first oh how I love it so, fresh and cool frost
  is now going.
'E mma' my mum calls as I gazed at the new flowers and babies
  that nature has given us.
A summer morning shimmers over my bedroom window
  like a breeze over a lake.
S o it turns darker and the nights get much colder.
O ctober brings autumn, a glorious time harvesting leaves
  falling with good food to eat.
N ovember passes and Christmas is here which helps us remember
  the joyful year.
S easons are such wonderful things, it's a good job that
  they never end.

*Emma Allen  (11)*
*Oldfield School*


## SUMMER TO WINTER

Summertime is hot,
Wintertime is cold,
I like it when it's shimmering,
I like it when it's snowing.

Summer's for shorts,
Winter for trousers,
Lollies are for summer,
Soup for winter.

Thickness is for winter,
Thinness is for summer,
Fires are for winter,
Fans are for summer.

*Holly Clarke  (11)*
*Oldfield School*

## The Beach Is . . .

The beach is sunny,
The beach is sunny
But is not funny,
For there's no clowns
Instead there's sandy mounds.

The beach is warm,
The beach is warm
But has no lawn,
For there's no grass.
Instead there's sand like glowing brass,
With specks of golden glass.

The beach is long,
The beach is long
And the waves pound as they hit the ground,
When the current is strong.

Even though people think it's wrong
I still like to surf along.

*Lydia Weikert  (11)*
*Oldfield School*


## In A Winter Wonderland

I see in the distance nothing but white,
In the sun a sparkle of blue
Catches my sight,
Snowflakes are glistening,
So bright.

As I look into the colourful sky,
My heart is filled with joy,
I find a tear in my eye,
As I stop and stare;
Aware that winter's beauty is here.

Now my winter wonderland,
Is muted,
As the snow starts to melt,
In the midday sun.

I think to myself
Next year, maybe next year . . .

*Rachel Parker  (11)*
*Oldfield School*


## BENJI OUR CAT

He is big fat fluffy
And round. He miaows
Loud and clear and
Doesn't have a fear.

He keeps me warm
In the night with
His snowy-white fur
And he often purrs.

When I go to school
He sits and sulks
But when I get back
He jumps and somersaults
And curls up on me.

Our family will always
Love him, whatever, whenever.

*Jessica Sargeant  (11)*
*Oldfield School*

## MONTY, THE MONKEY

I have a pet monkey,
His name is Monty.
He ate a whole pound of beef,
And acted like an Indian Chief.

He came from an African jungle,
I brought him from a car boot sale.
He is very smart,
I taught him to say, 'I want a jam tart.'

'Bye,' says my monkey,
Who is called Monty.
'Bye bye,' says me to him,
Now poor Monty will go for a trip, in a wheely bin!

*Saimah Alyas  (12)*
*Oldfield School*


## GUILTY

A vivid account of colours swirl in my mind,
With the buzz of silence and a twist of mystery,
A solid sound like a heartbeat,
Thumping through my soul,
My brain has taken the back door to deceit,
And left me here to recollect.

*Tara Davis  (13)*
*Oldfield School*

## CAT AND MOUSE

I know a little mouse
It lives in my house
It lives in a hole
With a very fat mole.

I also have a cat
It lives in my hat
It tries to eat the mouse
That lives in my house.

The mouse always tries to nick the cheese
But unfortunately he never succeeds
Because the cat is always about
So little mouse you'd better watch out.

So one day the mouse plots and schemes
Trying to figure out how to get the cheese
The mouse wakes up full of evil
He has a trick - anything but little.

Later in the afternoon
A bomb suddenly goes *kaboom*
So now the mouse can eat the cheese
You can tell how much he's pleased.

*Zobia Nadeem  (11)*
*Oldfield School*

## ARE YOU AS SCARED AS ME?

Please tell me,
Is it true that darkness can seep into your thoughts?
Are you as scared as me
Or do I stand foolishly alone?

Please tell me,
Is the world truly spinning?
Are you as scared as me
Or is it my hallucinating eyes?

Please tell me,
Is your implied hate real?
Are you as scared as me
Or are you lying, with your eyes shut?

Please tell me,
Are you as scared as me?

*Caroline Willatt (12)*
*Oldfield School*


## A POEM ABOUT GRAN

You can never make my gran happy
Did you encourage her to do her hair like that?
You can never make my gran happy
I should show you how to behave!
You can never make my gran happy
When I was young we could not do that!
You can never make my gran happy
When I was young I had to clean the house!
Well maybe one day I'll do something right.

*Kerry Davies (14)*
*Oldfield School*

## DOING HOMEWORK

I hate doing homework,
It is such a bore
Your parents always make you do it
But what is it really for?
Sometimes when I do my homework
I try and fall asleep
It's a good excuse for not doing it!
Writing, writing all the time
I have to work in overtime.
What's the point in working
When we've done it for five hours before?
We could be playing outside
Why oh why do we have to do homework?

*Charlotte Hinge  (13)*
*Oldfield School*


## THE ROAD

There's a road through the wood,
I don't know where it leads,
But I would like to find out if I could.

There's a road through the wood,
With no light at the end,
Not a twitter of birds,
Not a glimmer of words.

No one speaks of the road anymore,
They all think it's old and forgotten,
But one day I'll go back and see
Where the road leads.

*Harriet Pratten*
*Oldfield School*

## UNTITLED

Red, orange, yellow all mixed, trying to take charge
The heat is so strong you feel overpowered.
You die a hot death
With such hope
But it's too strong
Stronger than a sauna
Stronger than an oven
Stronger than you
Its power to kill could beat a knife
But no blood
Such a clever death
The remains are . . .
Fire.

***Verity Budd***
***Oldfield School***


## POOR WATER VOLE

They are building a wall
Down by the canal
Oh what will the poor vole do?
She's made a nice nest
One of the best
In a cosy hole too.

We'll move them today
The builder men say.
Let's take them to Slimbridge
For the wintertime.
They'll be just fine
Then they can come back in the spring.

***Katherine Miller  (13)***
***Oldfield School***

# FOR A SECOND OR TWO

One day when all troubles take over,
and hope has gone from our sight.
I will reach up to the sky one night
and bring down all the stars.
Peace will reign for a second or two
but all the real world will come flashing back to you
and troubles will return

One day when the day seems to have no end
and friends disappear in time
and you think your life is over
just remember that I'll be there for a second or two
to help and give you the spark
that you need
that'll help you through the next day
when the troubles will return.

One day when the world comes to a stop
the muddles and the troubles will be sorted
it will all slip into place
and on your mind nothing will be laid
And all will be forgotten.

But how about the next day?
What does lie ahead?
Troubles? Problems?
Unforgotten memories?
Don't fret, don't fear!
I'll still be there for just a second or two
to help you through the day.

*Abigail Hynam  (12)*
*Oldfield School*

## WELL, THAT'S FINE WITH ME!

They say dogs are a man's best friend,
They're loyal and faithful, well that's fine with me
But wait a minute, what about girls!
I suppose, as we're 'girlies' we'd need something small,
But, that's not the case with me!
It starts with his big rigid muzzle,
With little hairs that prickle my hands,
Up towards two little eyes, that shine, blue, with surprise.
A messy fringe, two pointy, pointy ears, and a mane as thick as a wig!
A long well set back, with a long tasselled tail,
Have you guessed yet?
Then I'll carry on.
Down his long slender legs to a set of
Milky white hooves, clip, clop, clatter, clatter,
Have you guessed yet? No, it's *not* a cow!
Alright, alright,
I'll tell you now, yes, you guessed it,
It's a horse!
So, men have their dogs,
That's fine with me!
But now I'll say
I've got my horse!
And that, I hope's,
Fine with you!

*Clare Hutton*
*Oldfield School*

## INSIDE

In my head
There is a voice
That wants to shout out
How I feel
And in my head
There is a child
Who pretends
Some things aren't real
I have a dream
To fly away
To disappear
When things get tough
But in my head
The voice it says
'Don't give up
If you've had enough
Just keep on going
for another day
Before you decide
To run away.'

*Louise Sigrist  (14)*
*Oldfield School*


## SHARING

Open the book that's where the magic lies
sit down get comfortable and feast your eyes
on magic, fighting,
adventure and daring,
but not just for you, books are for
*sharing.*

*Ezmy Curtis  (12)*
*Oldfield School*

## THE DOLPHIN

The dolphin glides through the waters blue
Jumps out does a twist looks like it flew,
Back in the sea the ocean deep
Lies so still looks like it's asleep.

The fish all swim beneath the sea
Knowing not about land, human or me,
But they do not know that death is to come
How sad it is to die so young.

There they lie in amongst the net
Men look on hungrily with no regret,
The dolphin swims throughout the sea
Could he be next for their tea?

Ten years on the sea is bare
No one at all took any care,
Like a graveyard there it lies
You can hear the ocean's cries.

*Leigh Anstey & Amy Coles  (13)*
*Oldfield School*


## THE PEACOCK

I once saw a peacock,
sitting on the wall,
it spread its tail feathers,
wide and tall.

It stood in the sunlight,
proud as can be,
with the colours of the rainbow,
glistening at me.

As I came nearer,
it was a joy to see,
the blues and the greens
shone radiantly, at me.

That beautiful peacock,
that I once saw,
stays in my mind,
and will for evermore.

*Charlotte Morris-Davies  (13)*
*Oldfield School*


## A LONELY CHRISTMAS

The time has come, once again,
Weather's turned cold, snowflakes fall,
Christmas shopping at the mall,
The Christmas tree's up, in the hall.

I'm looking out my window,
I'll tell you what I see,
Lots of children making snowmen
Happy as can be.

I'm walking down my road now,
Shops are brightly lit,
There's people passing by, in the cold,
Walking to where Christmas trees are sold.

It's quite a lonely time of year,
Because I'm on my own out here,
Waking up in my own old home,
To find myself all on my own.

*Helen Moore  (13)*
*Oldfield School*

## THOUGHTS

I wish Grandad was here! I wouldn't be so miserable and
wouldn't have to cry in my bedroom secretly - all the time!
People don't know how I feel about his death; they just think
'Oh, big deal! It's just another one of those things. You'll get over it!'
But it is a big deal and I can't 'get over it' . . . ever!
I couldn't even tell Mum and Dad how I felt even before he died -
when he was ill!

Sometimes I think to myself, 'Maybe I need help.
If I asked for counselling what would Mum think?
What would Dad think?
Maybe it might do me some good having someone to talk to.
Instead of being alone all the time in my room
Without a sister or brother my age to talk to, or to have their shoulder,
a comforting place for me to cry on whenever I feel down!'

But it won't happen, my dream won't come true,
A place of happiness just won't exist!

*Katie Smith  (13)*
*Oldfield School*


## THE SNOWMAN

The snow is melting I shall soon be dead.
It's getting warm in my icy bed.
It's warm now not cold.
The children don't treat me like gold.

I can't turn and hide,
There is no time for running.
I can't hitch-hike and get a ride
The sun is coming!

*Lucy Fry  (13)*
*Oldfield School*

# FOOD, FOOD

Sweets, sweets, I love sweets.
Sweets, sweets, they're delicious to eat.
Sweets, sweets they rot your teeth.
Sweets, sweets, I love sweets.

Ice-cream, ice-cream, I love ice-cream.
Ice-cream, ice-cream, tastes like a dream.
Ice-cream, ice-cream, is made from cream.
Ice-cream, ice-cream, I love ice-cream.

Toffee, toffee, I love toffee.
Toffee, toffee, I eat it with coffee.
Toffee, toffee, makes a good banoffee.
Toffee, toffee, I love toffee.

Popcorn, popcorn, I love popcorn.
Popcorn, popcorn, I eat it at dawn.
Popcorn, popcorn, pop the corn.
Popcorn, popcorn, I love popcorn.

Cake, cake, I love cake.
Cake, cake, it's easy to make.
Cake, cake, it must be baked.
Cake, cake, I love cake.

Buns, buns, I love buns.
Buns, buns, here I come.
Buns, buns, taste nice in your tum.
Buns, buns, I love buns.

*Emma Chamberlain (14)*
*Oldfield School*

# THE HOSPITAL

Double doors open wide
Various casualties are inside!
Tears glisten in the artificial light,
Some football hooligans start to fight!
Doctors rushing here and there,
White coats, tied back hair.
Bandages on the leg the arm,
A vicar comes to read a psalm!
Staggering in, blood on the floor,
Blood on my hands more and more!
Drip, drip, bleep, bleep,
Intensive care - sleep, sleep!
The eclipse my eyes, my eyes!
My friend told me I could look, she lied, she lied!
24-7-365
A & E here's to keep you alive!

*Katherine Nunn  (14)*
*Oldfield School*


# AUNTY ETHEL'S HAT

My Aunty Ethel's hat
Is a cross between a haggis and a cat.
It is fluffy and bright
And it glows in the dark at night.
It is pink, orange, purple and blue
Everywhere Aunty goes the hat goes too.
She carries it with her every day
People stop her in the street and say
I like your hat
I wish I had a hat just like that.

*Kirsten Davies  (13)*
*Oldfield School*

## FOR MY BELIEF

They'll never take me, not alive,
With their anti-Jewish view,
I'd fight Hitler to the end,
Than bow to biased rule.

I could've begged them for my life,
And shouted out my pleas,
But I'd rather die standing
Than live upon my knees.

We share the same almighty God,
And he looks down in pain,
To see one shoot the other dead,
For what? 'Tis all in vain.

I'd rather die and leave this world.
And pass into the next.
My youngest child will meet me there,
Our spirits then can rest.

What of those I leave behind,
My dearest wife, my joy?
How can fate be so unkind,
To take me from my boy?

The gun sounds 'bang', I see my blood,
I feel no pain, I feel no grief,
I have led a loyal life and
Stuck by my belief.

*Helena Carnegie  (14)*
*Oldfield School*

## THE MILLENNIUM

The millennium will bug people now
And farmers will milk virtual cows

The millennium isn't bugging me
I hope for the future and things I see

I hope for evil to come to an end
And every race to come and befriend

I want the millennium to bug all bullies
And stop them beating and hurting fully

I hope the millennium will bring good things
And remember good people and brilliant kings.

*Amy Hayward  (13)*
*Oldfield School*


## I WANT TO TRAVEL

When I grow up I want to travel
Around the world and see what I can see
Walk the lands and sail the seven seas
Go and see the cliffs of Dover
Go to Ireland and pick a clover
Across to France Normandy
Disneyland and Paris
I want to go to Egypt and see Tutankhamun
And maybe one day I will go to the moon.

*Jo Hutchison  (13)*
*Oldfield School*

## AROUND THE WORLD

I want to travel the world,
And see everything there is to see.

I want to go to Dover,
And pick a four leafed clover.

I want to climb the Alps,
And see if people can hear my yelps.

I want to swim the Atlantic,
But I bet I'll get all frantic.

I want to go to Turkey,
In hope I'll get all perky.

I want to go to Nigeria,
And see if it's like Algeria.

I want to go to China,
With tea from my mum's best china.

India, Australia, Tunisia, Paris,
And many more still to go!

*Tara Gregory  (13)*
*Oldfield School*

# Food

Cake is tasty
Don't be hasty
To eat it all up

Pie is yummy
In my tummy
With some tea in a cup

Fibre is vile
It gets rid of piles
So eat it all up

Cheese is a breeze
You don't have a squeeze
To eat it all up

Cream is a scream
It tastes a dream
I eat it all up

Chocolates are great to savour
That wonderful flavour
They definitely don't taste yuk!

*Joanne Barrett*
*Oldfield School*

# THE DEMON LIBRARIAN

I went to the library, picked up a book,
And began to thumb through it, just taking a look.
The librarian charged over, her face black as thunder,
I saw her expression, knowing I'd made a blunder.
'Just look at your hands!' she cried, 'Grimy and dirty!'
She spoke with contempt and was really quite shirty.
She continued, 'I dread to think where they have been!
They must be the grubbiest hands I have seen!'
I yelled, 'You think I'm dirty! You should see Daniel!'
(In case you don't know, he is my spaniel)
'He rolls in his whoopsies, he's only a pup,
And I·spent all this morning cleaning him up!
So if I am dirty, you just must excuse,
For I spent all this morning cleaning up poos!'
The librarian went purple, then snow-white, then green
She opened her foul mouth and started to scream:
'Get out, you animal! You must be insane!
You're no longer a member! Don't come back again!
Keep out! Keep out! No entry! No entry!
And don't sneak back in, cos I'll be on sentry!'
'My book's overdue,' I said, 'I owed you money.
I don't any longer - isn't that funny?'
Her eyes went all bloodshot. She towered over me.
I took to my heels and started to flee.
I spent all the money on sweets, crisps and chocs
I put them in a pretty box.
I gave the box to my dear ma,
Who asked how I afforded it - I just said, 'Ah-ha!'

*Katie Griffiths  (11)*
*Oldfield School*

# MY DAY!

At 8.30 the bell rings
We go to class where we all sing,
Soon as lunchtime comes our way
We know it's time to laugh and play.
At 3.10 the bell rings again
So we can all go home and go out again,
We meet our friends and have a chat
And go in when it gets black.

*Jo Gregson*
*Oldfield School*


## FUDGE

Guinea pigs are small and soft,
They snuggle inside your arm,
They are very calm.

They sit and gnaw with their tiny teeth,
They save their food from everyone else,
They love to play all day.

They stay in the corner of the hutch,
They hate to be caught,
They are masters at escaping.

They move about as fast as light,
With their sharp as knife claws,
They will cut some prison doors.

They get in the tiniest places,
A tube a hamster couldn't get in!
The only thing they are not good at is getting out.

*Max Humpston  (12)*
*Prior Park College*

## THE UNICORN

Here she sails in the night,
Her wings are glistening,
In the fiery light,
Her complexion is as white as a snowflake,
That glimmers in the cold, dark night,
Her horn is a symbol of power and strength,
That is now broken,
She remembers when they first met,
It was like a dream, a dream full of magic,
But dreams never last,
And here she is travelling to where her sun will set,
To where her destiny lies,
Where she will be reunited,
And where she must die.

*Antonia Robinson  (12)*
*Prior Park College*

## A GOLDFISH IN A BOWL

Why am I trapped in this awful glass sphere?
What is the meaning of my tiny life?
Destined to swim endlessly round and round.
Cramped, stuck forever in the oppressive bowl.
Humans goggling, eyes full of wonder,
While I am just swimming,
Swimming until I die.
A sorrowful life has a goldfish in a bowl.

*Emma Stubbs  (12)*
*Prior Park College*

## TODAY IS TOMORROW

A window is blown open by a hard wind.
I look behind me, but still I hurry on.
Faces on the wall look down disapprovingly on me.
I turn down another corridor, which seems to go on forever.
I turn another corner, and open another door.
Now I am looking around at the bleak darkness.
Something seems familiar although my mind is blank.
The darkness winds, and coils around me, like a snake
Waiting to pounce and take a bite at an unexpecting human.

I take a step forward, and another, then one more.
There is another door, I push it open and hurry in.
Now I look around me again, I can here a small buzz coming from
somewhere.
Now it is getting louder and louder, it is now more like a scream.
I look around me, quickly I must find another door.
There is no door, and there are no corners, I am trapped in a
Circular room, which is closing in on me.
Now I am falling faster, and faster, when I am going to stop
                                        I do not know.
I sit up and look around me, I am no longer in the huge dark house
                                        with endless rooms.
I am sitting at home safe in my bed.

*Mathilda Edwards  (12)*
*Prior Park College*

## STRIPES

The tigers laze around in the strong heat,
But a keen eye is waiting for any unsuspecting animal to cross its path,
Their beautiful striped coats shine in the sun,
As they playfully leap and fight.

The sandy plain ahead of them is a blur in the heat,
Soon they will make their journey,
Looking for their prey,
But now they are the prey, for the poachers are nearing.

The smell of danger is in the air,
Could these hunters become the hunted?
The terrifying rush increases and panic sets in,
All running in different directions the tigers begin to tire.
One more terrific leap and the poachers are lost,
The tigers are alone again.

*Emily Coles  (13)*
*Prior Park College*


## AUTUMN POEM

A young squirrel runs along a branch,
One leaf falls to the ground in a shade of colours in the orange
autumn sun,
He knows that autumn is coming,
He knows that mysterious, colourful season is coming to his home,
His great old oak tree is beginning to lose every leaf it possesses,
Now as the light begins to fade the little animal turns and scurries home
And sleeps for the rest of the year.

*Thomas Bury  (12)*
*Prior Park College*

## THE HUNTER'S INVASION

A bang, and all is still in the rainforest,
The parrots stop their endless gossiping,
The tree frogs still their leaping legs,
The brightly coloured lizards crawl silently to safety,
As they all hear the same sound,
The sound they have all learnt to dread,
The bang of a hunter's gun.
The huge striped body of the tiger
Bursts dramatically out of the bushes,
You can see her fury in her burning eyes.
The parrots spy at their penthouse suite,
A cloud of dust travelling swiftly over the dusty plains, their car.
The hunters, they may have guns and cars,
But they are no match for a loving mother,
They cannot reach the little striped cub they want for its beautiful coat,
For a mother's love is stronger than all the guns in the world.
But now here comes the tiger and her cub, in harmony,
They have each other's love,
Which is stronger than all the weapons in the world.

*Amie Corry  (13)*
*Prior Park College*


## FORBIDDEN LOVE

Forbidden love; deemed impossible,
Banned like a forbidden fruit,
An overpowering desire of secret lusting,
Warm hearted care with barbed wire barriers,
Painful; misunderstood.
As silent as the night,
As sinister as the dusk.
Frozen in fear
For the shameful discovery.

Distance is essential,
An everlasting longing,
Just out of reach like the birds,
Constant striving to reach true love,
Never succeeding, just failing
Banished like Romeo from Juliet,
A discreditable relationship never to contend.

*Cassie Palmer  (14)*
*Prior Park College*


## THE HAUNTED HOUSE

There's a house on the top of the hill,
My brother says it's haunted by the ghost of a murdered man,
But I know he's only trying to scare me.
The house is now derelict and forgotten,
Lost in another age.
I often look at it through my bedroom window,
The long narrow windows half-choked by the ivy,
And the crumbling, crooked walls covered in a mass of cobwebs.
My brother tells me that the man was strangled to death,
And that he still roams the house searching for his murderer.
Of course I don't really believe my brother,
The house has been empty for years and years,
Abandoned and neglected yet still standing,
Watching, yes, watching my every move.
I tell myself it's nonsense . . . after all
There's nothing sinister about that house, is there?
But even so I've never dared set foot in that house . . .
The house on the top of the hill.

*Jimmy Razazan  (13)*
*Prior Park College*

## ODE TO PUFF
*(And all other dragons)*

R iding on the back of Puff the magic dragon
I t really is every child's dream
D eep purple scales with an orange hint
I n and out of the stars Puff weaves
N ever do I look back at the mortal world
G riffins and the phoenix rise again

O nward we fly to a magical place
N ymphs and fairies dwell

P erfectly Puff slows to land
U p for one last swoop
F inally we gently fall
F alling
          Falling
                F
              a
                l
                  l
                    i
                      n
                        g to my marshmallow bed.

*Sian Gulliford  (12)*
*Prior Park College*

## THE BOX

Such a small object,
With unimaginable impact.
Viewers are hypnotised,
Without realisation.
Brainwashed by moving images.

As if the human race is brainless,
We believe what is fed to us.
And with what intentions?
For those who are taken in,
It is a form of entertainment.
Is the world taken in by the box?

*Lily House  (15)*
*Prior Park College*

## THE BLACK WIND

All of a sudden something came.
My life, dark and unhappy became.
I lost my friends and mind in one day,
Not even knowing if anyone will pray.

A black wind came into my life,
And it has made its place.
Without the intention of leaving,
It started to dictate my way.

As it blew into my face,
I began to feel the joy of ignorance and selfishness
And I fell into a deep nirvana.
A nirvana that lasted so long,
That it made my mind go completely wrong.

But one morning I woke up,
Feeling something on my body;
A wind, that felt gentle.
It wasn't the black wind,
It was God's spirit sending me a message,
Telling me that someone still loves me
And that my life is not a pile of worthless memories.

*Lea Stankovic  (14)*
*Prior Park College*

# MOONLIGHT

As night falls,
She draws her black cloak across the sleeping world.
No one knows why she comes
Or why she goes.
In the distance the bright lights
Shimmer like diamonds in the emptiness of the night.
Nothing is hear.
Everything sleeps under the velvet skies.
Shadows creep along the moonlit earth
Searching carefully
For something they'll never find.
The air is crisp and cool.
As it whirls silently by
It crinkles the falling leaves on this cool autumn night,
And the solitary moon looks down upon the sleeping world
Sad and lonely.

*Sophia Friedrich  (12)*
*Prior Park College*


# YOUR GAZE

Your gaze is like a misty haze,
Your lips with wrinkles make a maze.
You're the one who warms the morning,
You're the one that stops me snoring.

Your smile goes on for miles,
It can make any baby smile.
Your gaze is not a phase,
It never gets stuck in that maze,
It shines through that thick haze,
Yes, that is truly your gaze.

*Paul O'Hora  (13)*
*Prior Park College*

## MONSTERS

I know this might sound strange,
and slightly out of range,
but my younger sis is the one I never miss,
she pulls my hair,
she wees on my chair,
she pulls faces in a monster kind of way.

I think I'll move out,
if she doesn't do something about it,
as I feel like I'm stuck in a pit.
She dresses like a monster
and never looks right.
She talks like a monster
and sounds really bad.
If she doesn't sort it out,
I think I'll go
*Mad!*

***Georgia Edwards (11)***
***Prior Park College***


## AWAKENING

Materialism prevails, drawing a heavy mist
That clouds our vision.
Shallow herds contracted to continuing conformity,
Cloning a life of precision.

Survivors' invention for liberty
Is to grasp every chance,
Allowing them to awaken from their vacant state,
And the monotonous trance.

***Anna Travis (17)***
***Prior Park College***

## MONSTERS

Monsters can be big,
Monsters can be small,
Especially goblins and dragons
They've got it all.

There was an evil goblin and
His name was Grob,
Of course there came a knightly lad,
And pulped him into blobs.

There was another goblin,
His name was Bwup,
Along comes the courageous squire
And yes he's on a quest,
Poor old Bwup,
He didn't come off best!

*Alex Calkin  (11)*
*Prior Park College*


## THE ONE YOU LOST

Sometimes lying awake at night
You close your eyes and see their face
Emotions stir inside of you
Yet you know they're in a better place

So when you cry those tears
Shut your eyes
And think of all the memories
That you see inside
For nóthing loved is ever lost
And they were loved so much.

*Helen Le Gear  (15)*
*Prior Park College*

# AUTUMN

The icy, sharp wind has come again,
Branches endlessly waving frantically,
As the breeze accelerates for a final climax;

Trees filled with deep, emotional colours
Of reds, yellows, and browns,
Change their shades
And float down,
Swaying from side to side like a pendulum,
Onto the blanketed earth,
Conkers drop from the sky with a thud,
In their spiky, green shells.

The rustling of leaves starts once again,
As the hedgehogs gather their supplies,
Ready for the hibernation.
As the last leaf falls,
The once softened ground turns crisp and glazed white,
As the frost returns, over the forest floor;

The sun sets early below the naked trees,
Ready to face the start of a new day.

*India Humphreys  (13)*
*Prior Park College*


# EBBING AND FLOWING

A wave of fine blue velvet,
Crashes against a sharp sea wall,
A million birds are thrown into disarray,
The wave retreats,
And the birds return,
To scream at the approaching wave.

*Claude Harrison  (14)*
*Prior Park College*

## IT'S BUCKETING DOWN

The never ending water being poured
from that bottomless bucket they call the sky.
It turns streets to rivers
and cars to boats.
Lakes over-spill their temporary banks.
Sheep seek the high ground,
and ducks the low.
Then the lone shaft of light all alone
strikes the grey sky,
and bursts through,
then it ends,
and the boats go to cars,
and the rivers to roads.
Then it is over and the storm has come to pass.

*James Greene  (13)*
*Prior Park College*


## MONSTERS

M  onsters prowling round the distant lands,
O   nward it goes.
N  o one can stop it.
S  tand in its way and you will be sorry
T  rust it not.
E  yes are fiery yellow.
R  ough hair all over its body.

H  ell is where monsters come from.
E  very farmer fears him.
L  ots of muscles on his body.
L  ure him away from you.

*George Harper  (11)*
*Prior Park College*

## MONSTER POEM

In the night
Werewolves give
People a fright
Causing people to take flight.

At midday
People howl
For the zombie thrall
Come to stay.

In the night
Grendel's might
Can only be stopped by
Beowulf in a fight.

When vampires come
People hide,
Not scared of death
But death is defied.

Sometimes dragons take flight
To make a deadly dive
On an unsuspecting
Questing knight.

*Adam Kington  (12)*
*Prior Park College*

## River Lion

Peacefully snoozing,
The waves cradle the boats.
A harmless lion sleeps,
Composed and content.
But then it awakens,
Mischievous and impish;
With a desire to play.
As he innocently rocks the boat,
Getting more and more troublesome.
He starts tossing and turning,
Fidgety and anxious;
Prowling and growling.
But soon the lively lion,
Is peaceful once again.
He lays down his drowsy head,
Stretching out his velvet paws,
Onto the riverbed.

*Natalie Dicorato (13)*
*Prior Park College*


## Blesséd Be

Blesséd be sincerity
let flawless pain outroar,
Blue fatality,
The pain of bloody war.

A certain sea catastrophe
A scarlet time of hate,
Those withheld in mystery ·
Belong to journey's fate.

*James Brake (16)*
*Prior Park College*

# THE RACE OF TIME

Time is running a race,
She began with the blast of a gun.

Come watch the race,
Before time wins,
Appreciate life,
Before she crosses the tape.

See her feet go,
So steady and stable,
Not faltering once,
Or flagging at all.

Listen from your cradle,
Take heed of the fable.
Plod on like the tortoise,
Don't fall like the hare.

'Don't wish time away'
That's just what they say.
Treat every moment
As the very last day.

Time is running a race,
She is running, running, running

Running the 'human race' . . .

*Alexia Sophie Hereford  (14)*
*Prior Park College*

# TIME

Time
We run on it
We are the train and time the track.
From the day that we are born
In the primeval dawn of life,
Time condemns us to the horror and inevitability of death.

If we were to master time
We could do anything;
Make your favourite moments hang golden and suspended
Or make the agonisingly slow boring days
Whizz by like a roller-coaster ride.
The infinite possibilities which time can bestow
If only one could harness it.

But while time stretches inexorably on,
Treating with equity both the beggar and the king.
It circumscribes the span of the gift of life,
Bringing the limitations of day and night
Making us old by the second.

But what does this matter,
If we accomplish all that we set out to do?
Our soul, our spirit, our essence
Will travel eternally along the track of time.

*Scott Shepherd  (13)*
*Prior Park College*

# LOVE

Love, love is a strange thing indeed,
when you say love it can mean many things,
boys dream of pin-ups, girls dream of knights,
waiting for that one,
that is what most people believe.

Love can be used to mean of family,
love can be used in terms of favourites,
but whatever you use, love will still be special,
because life without love would be a strange thing indeed.

If there was no love in the universe,
no one would be happy,
there would be no laughter, no joy,
no fun at all,
because life without love would be a sad thing indeed.

*Olivia Hussey (13)*
*Prior Park College*

# SPIDERS

Spiders, spiders are creepy and crawly,
Spiders, spiders can be beautiful,
Spiders, spiders can be poisonous,
Spiders, spiders can be harmless,
Spiders, spiders are furry,
Spiders, spiders have long legs,
Spiders, spiders, keep them away from *me!*
*Spiders!*

*Jeremy Morris (12)*
*Prior Park College*

## THE GREAT BOOKSTORE

I open the door
to the great bookstore.
I saw at the counter
a man who would flounder
around the dog on the mat,
which had squished his hat.

I looked at the bookshelf
and saw a story about an elf.
It was quite amusing.
Then I saw the man boozing,
I yelled, 'Stop that'
and he shouted back,
'Mind your own business mate
I've got a date!'

I went to the back
and found a vat
of strange drink,
which had a great stink.
The smell was musty,
the label was dusty.
I opened the top
and there was a pop.
I drank a bit.
Then it was quick
to kill me dead,
I fell and hit my head.
I was live no more
and that was my trip to the great bookstore.

*Duncan Dawson  (13)*
*Prior Park College*

## UNTITLED

Screaming engine revs,
Wheels spinning,
Tasting intensely thick petrol and dust, choking the mind.
Smelling hot dogs, onions, coffee and rubber,
Feeling nervous, excited, impatient.
Wishing, longing to be in that car.

Pole position,
Clenching the steering wheel;
Pushing my back deep into the seat,
Gritting my teeth.
Squeezing the throttle.
Right foot gently down, playing with the revs,
Hand on the clutch, feathering it,
Lights go red - down goes the throttle, focus!
Lights go green - out goes the clutch
Panic, adrenaline engulfs my body - is it a good start?

The battle begins,
Last on the brakes, first into the corner.
A concentrated mind, surrounded by chaos.
Desperate to stay calm as my heart races,
Cars fly off.
Endless circuits on and on battling furiously.

The flag, the champagne,
Exhaustion, relief;
Dreaming of winning, never of losing!

*Andrew Edwards  (14)*
*Prior Park College*

# INDIAN SUMMER LOVE

He granted my every thought unsung
A seemly melody,
And oh, so tenderly with unfurling tongue -
Guided his words to those stricken dumb.

With his love a blossom three times came,
And all rime became rosiness.
Then, each dewy eye no longer rained
For I was his ever fermenting sun.

Yet today, a quenchless redolence gone astray -
Remains only so memories can be bred,
For love will linger just like the trees,
When the summer flowers are dead.

*Rachael Canter  (16)*
*Prior Park College*


## ALPINE

Azure ice lake
Crisp, white light
A something in an Alpine sky

Vivacious: green
Rest her for eternity
With my Alpine sky

A white sky
A white snow
A black rock

How, overhead a buzzard soars
Plucking at our immortality
Shredding our new found destiny.

*James Carlin  (16)*
*Prior Park College*

## THE OPPRESSED

The oppressed will grow more determined,
By each day subjected to torment,
Their power to increase
And battle those tyrants which oppress them.

Their hope hard to crush,
Will stand resolute and strong,
Feeding from each other's courage
And casting its seed to all.

Until in fiery glory they rise,
Like the phoenix from the ashes,
Enlightening the shadows of all those oppressed,
And burning brighter than before.

*Iain Clarke  (16)*
*Prior Park College*


## LIFE SUPPORT

Omniscient figures loomed up before me
As the last waves created their last sweep
Across my body,
Oblivious of the movement around me,
I sought the kind hand which seemed to lead me.

Overwhelming darkness clambered into my thoughts
The incontinuous pounding stopped.
Creating a peaceful tide, a pause, a poise.

As my mind fluttered to a halt,
The omniscient figures faded to a memory,
And all movement came to a halt
And quivered in front of me.

*Verity Spikes  (16)*
*Prior Park College*

# THE VICTIM

All of them crowding,
I'm suffocating, trapped.
Heart racing, blood pounding,
As they gather to mock.

And they seem to be like
Some flock of fierce vultures,
Swooping in turn to
Tear at my flesh.

Their jeering voices merge into one,
And I taste their hatred on the air.
I curl into a protective ball,
Shielding myself from their cruel, harsh words.

Then the blessed trill of the bell -
Finally my saviour has come.
The melange dissolves and fades and
I'm left to my arduous thoughts.

I slide to the floor, trembling,
As relief floods down my cheeks,
In vast, wet rivers that meander and twist
And escape from me to the floor below.

And now all that I am able to do
Is to wait, in dread,
For tomorrow's feed.

*Natasha Bruce  (14)*
*Prior Park College*

# CAT

I woke and yawned
And sniffed the air,
Another rainy day
Is what I did fear.

I bounced down the stairs
And out the cat flap,
Already I thought it was time for another nap.

I smelt a mouse,
And before I had time to turn for the house,
I was on the chase for the poor defenceless mouse.

I saw it running back to hide,
Unfortunately for him it was time to die.

Up I jumped and pounced upon him,
He squeaked and struggled,
But I was determined to win.
One loud crunch,
And a quick, sharp munch.

After my snack,
I wandered towards the cat flap.
Back in time for my mid-morning snack.

*Rebecca Wakefield  (13)*
*Prior Park College*

## THE HEDGEHOG

I sniffed,
The air was rank, the ground was grey,
And great blocks of stone rear into the sky,
I am hungry,
No snails, no slugs,
So I snuffle about.
The moon is up,
It casts a faint light,
But lights are everywhere now,
They hurt my eyes.
I trap a worm,
And nibble it,
I'm still hungry and thirsty,
I amble along in a daze.
The ground starts shaking,
I curl in a ball,
I am being lifted,
Thrown,
Caught,
I'm flying,
I don't know what's going on,
I plummet,
My life flashes before my eyes,
I land
On something soft,
My spikes pierce,
A shriek,
A curse,
And words too rude for a hedgehog,
Escape into the night.

I roll,
Over and over,
I slow down and stop,
I unroll and blink in the light,
I can smell slugs and water,
I'm set up for the night at least.

*Emma Geen  (12)*
*Prior Park College*


## OPEN DAY

A sunny October morning, it was our Open Day,
It happens once a year, to prove that we're OK.

We wore best blazers, white shirts and a smile,
While we toured the school, mile after mile.
There's a lot going on, needless to say,
Even six French maids serving café au lait.

The kids looked so small
Could we have been like that?
Why didn't Ralph build his house where the grounds are nice and flat?

They toured each classroom looking at every file,
Weighing up the pros and cons of our Georgian pile.

There's basketball, singing and music all day,
While the artists made a chair from papier maché.

I wonder what they thought of us?
I wonder if they'll come?
I could be a prefect then,
But for now my job is done!

*François Bonnet  (14)*
*Prior Park College*

# THE WAR POEM

'Fire at will' shouted the squadron leader,
recoiling a chorus of bangs, shouts and groans,
in pain, a whiplash of speeding bullets entered penetrated flesh.

Explosions everywhere as giants of the artillery massacre
those in trenches.
Sounds of pain entered the heads of those still standing, more friends
fell at my side as we advanced toward hell on earth, and a place
we dare not go.

Huge bulks of metal stomped through the smoke, giving no care to
what was lying before them, nothing slowing them down.
The sound of cracking bones as if it were walking on crackling leaves,
the tank advanced noisily.

I saw this destruction and thought 'What are we fighting for?
Our lives or our sanity?'
I wondered why we were killing people who don't want to fight.
I wanted to go to bed!

*Alex Pierce  (14)*
*Prior Park College*

# BETRAYAL

A promise means but nothing,
Just waves of wasted breath,
Lest every word is carved in stone,
And honoured until death.

To break a vow to one you love,
Shall rip the bond apart,
Never to be whole again,
A scarred but beating heart.

*Siobhan Rogers  (16)*
*Prior Park College*

# REALITY STRIKES

The green hills, carpeted with sugared blades of
grass, roll across the land.
The blue river, glinting gently in the fresh morning
light, flows gracefully.
The yellow sunlight, turning the land of glinting gold,
shines brightly down.
The white clouds, soft as buds of fluffy cotton wool,
float above effortlessly.
The purple flowers, with fresh delicate green leaves,
unfurl their tiny petals.
And, as night comes, the sky is alight with a thousand
diamonds.

But . . .

The time goes by and all is lost.
The green hills turn to brown, the grass claws at me
with its sharp, spiteful fingers.
The blue river turns to grey, tossing and churning its
bed as it cuts into its bank.
The yellow sunlight is no longer bright; its beams
reach not through the smog.
The white clouds turn to black; they tower above me
like huge terrifying giants.
The purple flowers turn to weeds; their toughened
blooms now take over the land.
And, as I open my eyes, the dream is now reality.

*Laura Clarke  (14)*
*Prior Park College*

## POEM OF A SOLDIER

Cold, wet, mud hugging me tight.
Screaming shell fire all day and all night.
The blaze of the guns and the screams of your friends.
When will this terrible, bloody war end?

The fresh smell of blood flows through the air.
Fleas and cockroaches crawl through your hair.
Our boots are full of holes and our clothes all smell.
When can we leave this place they call hell?

Now the rain has come.
Now the snow starts to fall.
Like a million bodies shot against a wall.
We wake each day under a layer of frost.
Are we fighting for victory or fighting for loss?

Now a cloud of gas passes overhead.
By the time it's gone there's two more dead.
You can hear the screams as their lives drift away.
Are we digging our trenches or digging our graves?

*Tom Ross  (14)*
*Prior Park College*


## STATIONERY LOVE

Love is like a pencil case
It can be pointless - a broken pencil
It can be pointed - a sharpener
It can be erased - a rubber
It can be blue - a biro
It can be transparent - a ruler
It can be complex - a calculator
It can be forever - a compass.

*Dave Fraser  (15)*
*Prior Park College*

# CLOSE ENCOUNTER

I dived down into the deep ocean,
Here I stopped and saw fish so beautiful,
Orange, green, red and blue,
So many colours I could not name.

But to my horror and fright,
Behind me I saw a great white,
His jaws opened wide,
I decided to hide.

But he was too fast,
I didn't want to harm him,
But I had no choice,
I turned around and shot,
I swam away and hid among the coral.

Ten more killers came from the sea,
But this time they weren't after me.
The big great white was up again,
But the odds were against him,
One against ten.

I took my chance to escape,
I kicked and pulled my hardest,
I saw them chasing me, gaining on me,
With one last pull I was safe.

Looking down at the sea,
Glad, those ten horrors had not got me.
They chased the white through the blood-red blue,
Then they gave the great white what was due.

*Oliver McGivern  (12)*
*Prior Park College*

## CLAUSTROPHOBIA

I am hidden
hidden from view into obscurity,
my mind, once a precious instrument
is now relegated into a manipulative tool.
My clothes, once a sign of individuality
are now a sign of captivity.
My face is no longer mine,
it is swept clean and in place is a charade,
the emotion once shown on it is now a mere contrivance of the past.
The only feelings expressed are those of my captors,
my actions are monitored,
all words recorded.
On my feet are the shoes of one hundred thousand people.
No longer am I characteristic,
decisions are no longer me,
old is disused and abandoned.
Curiosity is permanently lost,
just as I am.
I am the product of my own problem,
I am a robot,
after all I am an insecure inner city yuppie.

*Katherine Upton  (15)*
*Prior Park College*


## ANGEL

Static spun-gold hair
Frames a wondering face
Sweet lips and wide eyes
Perfect grace

Pulsating glory
As flaming she passes
White porcelain feet
In dew-beaded grasses.

*Emmaline Peters  (13)*
*Prior Park College*

## THE MISSING PAST

A room filled with voidness,
A place as empty as a vacuum.
No future, no present, no past,
Just the feeling of nullity.

The touch of bareness is clearly felt,
As feelings and pains are unknown.
The ceiling above, and the walls aside,
Draw nearer as time goes by.

The increasing temptation of adventure,
Becomes painfully unbearable,
When just outside the doorway,
Time is ticking away.

The floor wearingly sighing,
In the usual rhythm of boredom.
The non-existing window,
Replaced by a hard cold wall.

An unsuitable place for pleasure,
An unsuitable room for life.
Life containing pleasure or hatred,
This room containing nothing.

*Celine Besseling  (14)*
*Prior Park College*

## CARPE DIEM

When the sky changes to smouldering grey and the bubbling
                                                brooks run dry,
When the birds' chirping comes to an end and the lush vegetations die,
When our voices cannot utter and the judges cannot condemn,                  .
Will we up arms and say if only 'carpe diem',
When we open the eyes of the blinded will we keep the
                                                promises made,
Will we dream the dreams of the past or will we try the things forbade,
When we lose a treasured person will we recall each strand of hair,
Regret things we should have done; need to be sure they know we care,
Wish that we had shared not only prayers of requiem,
But show no sorrow, do not weep, next time 'carpe diem',
Wait not for eternity, agony of regret is hard to pay,
Live to live, remember, 'carpe diem' seize the day.

*Harriet-Kate Owen  (14)*
*Prior Park College*


## DIFFERENT

This animal roams and tears up the Earth,
Crumbles and cracks homes.
It waits impatiently for its food to die
And then it carelessly takes it down
Into the underground life of tunnels,
Where it eats its find,
Then carries on destroying the underworld.
This gentle beast is prey to many shy animals,
So what is this animal so strange?
Well, it's a worm,
Nothing is plain.

*William Akerman  (12)*
*Prior Park College*

## HOPEFUL SERENITY

Hope knows no peace
Yet his constancy is true
He dances in the dappled light
And flits across the blue

He plunges into sorrow
Then transcends to shimmering heights
He blankets me in warmth
On starless cimmerian nights

Love, honour and freedom breathe joy
Yet it is in hope alone,
In that hot, deep serenity
That all my dreams are borne.

*Katie Edwards  (17)*
*Prior Park College*


## WHO AM I?

Whilst a hazy world endures
I'm distinction in the vague
In a desert of dismay
I'm the shadow of a shade

Whilst the seasons ebb and flow
I'm the constant in the changed
Though composed of flesh alone
I'm the tune that's rearranged

Whilst engulfed in tides of light
I'm the darkness of your mind
In a crowd of ceaseless fears
I'm the face you'll never find.

*Timothy Richards  (17)*
*Prior Park College*

## DRAGON

Her heavy eyelids opened.
She was in a cave, imprisoned by the evil wizards.
She knew this, as she knew she must escape.
Bracing her legs, she stood.
Her powerful wings spreading out, to brush against the sides of the small cave.
Her eye caught a small black bundle in the corner.
Her babe was sleeping.
She knew she had to protect him.
Taking him outside would be risking death for the sweet little thing.
He should stay here.
She stooped and crawled over.
Reaching her babe she watched him with love in her eyes.
She nudged him with her nose.
There was no response.
She nudged him again.
She was afraid.
Gently she pushed him over, onto his back.
His eyes were staring up at her, not seeing.
Tears of helplessness and grief slid down her face from her big, cloudy eyes.
Her babe was dead.
Murdered by the people.
She remained there crying for a long time.
After all the tears had run out, she knew what she must do.
She gave way to anger.
They had no right to do this.
She took to the sky.
Ripping the magical chains from the walls with the strength of her emotions.

Her body screamed in pain.
She ignored it.
She sped towards their camp.
Towards revenge . . .
. . . and her death.

*Rosie Lewis  (12)*
*Prior Park College*


## TOGETHER IN THE WIND

The sky tears above me
And the thunder pitches through
The pulsating clouds as they sweep in waves
Across the panicked moon.
He stands before me,
The wind plucking at his clothes
And rain spraying his cheeks with froth,
But nothing can hide the sadness in his eyes
As they bleed into mine.
The sky falls suddenly
And with it my tears,
Rising to embrace the cruel earth.
The air churns,
Choking and silent.
We stand in understanding,
The winds mingling our thoughts
Healing our wounds.
And then with the lull of the wind
He is gone,
And I stay in my desolation,
Alone, at the heart of the storm.

*Camilla Szymanowska  (15)*
*Prior Park College*

# 4 SEASONS

The nights are darker and yet dazzling lights glow,
The air is silent like the never ending hush of death,
The ground become crisper like clean linen sheets,
Winter, winter is here.

The sun breaks through the blanket of clouds,
Flowers spurt with vibrant colour,
The green leaves awaken like a child on Christmas Day,
Spring, spring is here.

The days are long and yet nights are short,
The air is filled with the scent of flowers,
The earth is full of life like the colour red,
Summer, summer is here.

The leaves turn to bright red and yellow,
The days are shorter, fresh air is scarce,
The leaves crunch as you walk like the crunch of boiled sweets,
Autumn, autumn is here.

*Jennifer Castley  (13)*
*Prior Park College*


# IN THE COMPANY OF INSANITY

Eternal bliss in darkness stand,
And ride the flow of fear.
Surrender to internal parasite,
Forgetfulness of tear.

Blind the eye of the mind,
Fortify the soul,
In the company of insanity,
If thoughts are never told.

*Harry Woloszynski  (17)*
*Prior Park College*

## COLOURFUL BLACK

Outside the adamant wind is hurtling through time
And the dried-up, cracked brown leaves lie swept aside,
As though by an angry hand.
Fickle clouds totter unsteadily,
As silence's tumultuous row augments fiercely.

The musky smell of charcoal
Drifting amongst the ashes of yesterday
Still lingers, suspended in the air.
The light from the untamed fire still glows bright;
Welcomes you into is passionate arms.

Come into the warmth of the heat, so divine and irresistible.
You wish to stretch out and entrust yourself
To the crackles from those wild orange flames
As they gently send you to sleep,
Singing to you a bittersweet lullaby.

But fire can destroy and engulf its lovers in a deathly conflagration,
Grimly digging their deep, bottomless graves.
Dividing soil from earth with a sharp relentless shovel, severing away
their souls.
So sometimes it is better to brave the savage storm,
The colourful black, which batters so cruelly at the door.

*Siobhán Kelly  (15)*
*Prior Park College*

## THE LOSS OF INNOCENCE

Let me cut a bit of your mind,
Let me keep it forever,
I won't let them take it,
I won't let them tear it apart, pervert it and change it.

I will keep it in my box of minds,
And I will protect it,
From the evil civilisation.
I won't let it be clever,
I will keep it as stupid,
I won't let it see hell,
Just heaven.

Let nature guide you,
And the people won't harm you,
Live in a fairy tale like Adam and Eve
Once did.

Their minds are not pure,
They have been tainted forever,
They've learned to love and to hate,
They fight to the top;
Of what?
Futility.
And the only way back,
Is the end,
To get out of the misery.

*Olesia Bogdanova  (15)*
*Prior Park College*

## TILL DEATH DO US PART

It was a quiet evening,
I was lying on the floor,
It was a quiet evening,
When he first walked through the door.

It was a sunny morning,
We were lying in the dark,
It was a joyous morning,
And our day had yet to start.

It was a quiet evening,
When we talked together, we,
He said, 'We shall make a pledge
To be together for eternity.'

It was a quiet evening,
I lay weeping on the floor,
Lying with the knowledge,
That I would see him no more.

It was a quiet morning,
I sat sobbing by the sink,
With his pills beside me,
And took my final drink.

It is a quiet morning,
As I lie here on the floor,
With him here beside me,
And we'll lie here forever more.

*Majella Munro  (15)*
*Prior Park College*

## STREET LIGHT

I step out onto the dripping wet street -
Deceased and silent after the storm;
Like a tarmac sea that is flat -
Without waves or sound.

Neither does the wind blow -
Not a wisp stirs the fir peaks of the trees.
Red glow of a street lamp reflects the newly polished road;
A pool of calm soft light;
Reflecting the road's dark hardness.

The air was still -
Suspended there:
Holding its breath;
Listening to the silence,
We listened back with great intent.

*Jonathan Brett  (14)*
*Prior Park College*


## SOMEDAY

Someday I'll be famous
Everywhere my face will be seen

Someday I'll make a movie
I'll get a record deal
I'll make millions

Someday I'll play basketball in the NBA
Someday I'll be president of the USA

I'll cure world hunger
Someday.

*Ben Hill  (15)*
*Prior Park College*

## WEEKDAY MORNING

Six fifty-nine and all is still
The room remains silent
And lifeless.
As silent and as lifeless
As a graveyard where all is hushed
Other than the bird
Calling in the trees.

The clock turns seven,
The radio breaks the silence.
The graveyard is destroyed,
A noisy city put in its place . . .

. . . A place that was once silent
And lifeless . . .

A voice is heard from the radio,
Stopping only when a hand
Lazily reaches out
Of the nest of bedclothes.

A figure grumpily gets out of bed
And yawns a long yawn . . .

Yet another school day!

*Chris Constantine  (15)*
*Prior Park College*

## WAITING . . .

I sit in the silence of the cold.
The hard wind stinging my face.
I wait for him.

The trees whistling my name
in the distance.
The leaves rustling a song.
I wait for him.

Time has passed.
Nobody has come.
Daylight has sprung
out of the dewy morning.
I wait for him.

Another day,
another week,
another year.
The birds sing
with the trees and wind
like a band playing a symphony.
As I wait for him.

*Kate Ralls  (14)*
*Prior Park College*


## MONSTERS

A monster is a peculiar thing,
They can be fat they can be thin,
They can be fun or they can be scary,
But of them, you must be very wary.

Some monsters have sharp fangs and claws,
Some monsters just have hairy paws,
Some live inside a dark, damp cave,
Some just don't know how to behave.

In days of old the dinosaur did roam,
Over the land we now call home,
If they were all alive today
Jurassic Park would be the place to stay.

I'd like a monster for a pet,
We'd have wild parties that we'd never forget,
My friends would all come round to see
My monster pet and his best pal, me!

*Carl Hills  (11)*
*Prior Park College*


## A DARKENED WORLD

I stand alone,
A mere shadow,
In the eternal darkness,
Afraid to be noticed.
I stand in the darkened corner,
A social cast off.

My life lives on,
In my own secluded world.
I am caged in loneliness,
Encased in disaster,
As I watch the world go by.

The shadows close in,
The people fade away.
I am left alone,
Lost in a web of insanity,
When the sun has gone to sleep,
And the frost returns once more.

*Charlotte Harrison  (12)*
*Prior Park College*

# MY BELOVED SISTER

I saw her first through wavering candlelight,
My sister in her cradle an hour old;
Outside, the snow was drifting through the night,
But she lay warm, oblivious to the cold.

Her eyes were closed, the half-moist wisp of hair,
A honey harvest on her wrinkled head,
The smile upon her face, as if she was elsewhere
But she knew the land she had inherited.

The white lily will be her shirt,
It suits her body best;
With cornflowers in her hair,
A red rose on her breasts.

Her gloves will be marigold,
Glittering on her hand;
Her dress will be sweet-william,
That grows upon the bank.

And she my winter sister, does she know?
If I were a poet
I'd write poems for her.
If I were a musician
Music too.
But as I'm only an average girl
I give her my only love
As best I can.

*Selina Lu Siew Sui  (15)*
*Prior Park College*

# REMEMBER ME

Remember me. I am not far away,
I will always be in your heart to stay,
Think of the fun times we have had together,
And not the sad times that felt like forever.

Please do not cry or grieve,
Imagine I am just going away and not going to leave,
I will visit you in your dreams,
Remember I'm still here, remember I'm still here.

Remember me with a happy face,
And not looking like disgrace,
Think of us running through the fields,
With smiles on our faces, which run from eye to eye.

Do not forget me. I will always be near.
You may not be able to touch me,
But you will be able to see me . . .
In your thoughts and in your dreams.

Think of me having fun,
In a place which people call heaven.
Remember I will always miss you,
But I ask of you one favour, just . . .

Remember me, remember me.

*Victoria Ellis-Jones  (14)*
*Prior Park College*

## The Storm

The clouds writhed in agony,
The black sky oozed like blood,
The rain crashed down like a waterfall,
The sky tumbled and swirled,
An array of colours - purples and reds,
Then suddenly a flash of anger and a painful roar,
A bolt of death was spewed
From the heaving monster,
The earth lit up with a sudden flash,
And shook with an agonising roar,
The droplets stopped pounding the floor,
The roaring ceased,
The deadly strikes became timid,
The writhing clouds grew calm,
A warm red glow filled the clouds,
A wonder I could not fathom.

*Sarah Hobbs  (13)*
*Prior Park College*


## Monsters

B  lurgorbs are horrible, red and rude,
L  eaving no place clean,
U  nder the hills they plot plans that are shrewd,
R  unning round mountains unseen.
G  oing into towns, their slimy scales shine,
O  ver cities they blunder and fall,
R  oaring and saying that 'everything's mine',
B  y the way they're very tall!

*David Whitaker  (11)*
*Prior Park College*

# LOVE

The deity that placed me
in this paradise,
had forgotten
but just one thing,
that reward of its most ornamented tree,
satenically awaited
mankind's adversary.

This creature
sought me out,
with relentless
sapphire tarnished eyes,
and coiled upon me with empty embraces,
and soft
seductive smiles.

Mightier, now the beast
lunged for my heart,
but before
the final sinews were torn,
I helplessly cried out for a name,
a haunting whisper lingered:

- 'Love'.

*Charley Heffer  (16)*
*Prior Park College*

# THE DYING DEAD

Splashes of crimson tear the course concrete earth,
A menagerie of green, white and gold,
Fluctuate from the rubeous exordium,
A culture of traditions to sanctify.

A culture of traditions to suppress,
The stream flows thicker by the day,
Tarnishing the wounded rolling hills,
Ploughing the tender chapped soil.

An effervescent torch of hostility burns,
Piercing the lonely souls of those who care,
The atrabilious clouds eclipse the saving sun,
Seizing the glory of the dying dead.

*Benedict Davies  (16)*
*Prior Park College*


# THE SWEETNESS OF THE SIN

I thought this was love,
I gave myself to him,
His taste was in my mouth,
The sweetness of the sin.

The brightness hurt my eyes,
The heat was pure pain,
I suddenly realised my mind,
The feeling was insane.

Skin on skin we touched,
A contract signed in lust,
Burnt by the fire of him,
The love turned into dust.

*Annabel Pitts Crick*
*Prior Park College*

# Riddles Of Immortality

Let me not wake you,
By an exacerbated thought -
In places, of fragmented time.

Is pity which you feel,
Devoid of emotion -
By autonomous imagery.
To subjugate senses -
By soporific illusions.

Abstruse ideas -
Unquestioned assumptions.
Settle immovably by my side,
A thief, lay heavy sleep -
Descending into my heart.

In it judgement be,
Clouded by dignity.
A malicious marksman -
Condemned to be, yet undemonstrative.

So we must meet -
As separate entities,
By discernible floors,
Widespread in morality -
A paradigmatic form of certainty.

*Vincent Burke  (17)*
*Prior Park College*

## TRANSCENDING NORMALITY

Immersed by the azure abyss above,
Which infinity herself could not stop.
Her immense empyrean
Which engulfs eternity,
Mesmerises me.

As the heavens seize my being,
The Lilliputian unfolds.
My existence invades oblivion,
Her magnificence renders me
So meaningless.

Since then,
I could have lived a lifetime again,
It matters not to me.
But to encounter such liberation,
Was deliverance herself.

*Kate Kimber  (16)*
*Prior Park College*


## THE AMAZON RAINFOREST

The Amazon is a fantastic wonder,
From there the rainforest is over yonder,
With snakes and bats and coconut trees,
And millions and millions of Brazilian bees.

There's the sloth on the vine,
Hanging there very divine,
Monkeys in the bongo tree,
Here you can run wild and free.

The Amazon is a dangerous place,
There are many fears to face,
Lions and Tigers and poisonous plants,
And tribal men doing their dance.

This is an area in peace and quiet,
Away from the city noise and riot,
Nowhere near the cars, you'll see,
This really is the place to be.

*Nicholas Stuart  (11)*
*Prior Park College*


## COBWEBS

Some cobwebs
Have dewdrops of pearl and diamond
Stolen from the rings of happy engagements,
And pinioned to a shadowy bridal veil;
Caught in a tangled web of knitting,
Silver-spun and shadowy.
Imagination and reality combine in a glistening basket,
Innocent - Deceiving,
Enticing - Relieving of all earthly cares
The spider, caught in its own web;
And longing for the freedom of dusty corners
Where no breezes blow,
Where, long untouched by human hands or sighs;
He once learned to knit, and sew
Those fragile curtains of gossamer,
Strung beneath two needles
On the branch that holds him now,
Caught like a fish in his own net.

*Sophie Reynolds  (14)*
*Prior Park College*

## MILLENNIUM FEVER

As the millennium approaches and the Dome and Ferris wheels
are put up,
There is no surprise of its arrival
As the world begins to go corrupt
It's like a surprise on Christmas morning
When you don't know what's downstairs
Some are excited
And some are around the bend
Who will have the first baby?
And whose computer will crash first?
Nobody knows, until Big Ben clongs first
The millennium may be exciting
The millennium may be dull
The millennium may have changes
That no one would have been ready for up till now
Roll the red carpet
Get the champagne ready to explode!
The millennium's on its way
Not too long to wait now
It's just around the corner
It is almost in sight
People are excited
About the fantastic millennium night.

*Andrew Brooks  (15)*
*Prior Park College*

## UNTITLED

Her hooded eyes lie half-closed
Hunched shoulders submerged into her chair
Withered face leaning on the heavy crushed velvet
Grey strands of twisted hair disguise her neck
Eyes perfectly still, gaze into nothingness

A tear-jerking life plays in her mind
A tap drips on in the background
Patterns on the wallpaper dance like wild heathen in the night
Alluring ghosts draw her closer
Eyes perfectly still, gaze into nothingness

Fairies softly tiptoe on her lips
She is blinded by a perfumed bliss like no other
Temptation blows her kisses from his honeydew lips
*Eden isn't far, my darling*
Eyes perfectly still, gaze into nothingness

*Is it worth holding on?*
Deep, hoarse breathing carries like a metronome
*It's going to be difficult darling, come with me instead*
The voices swim, the furniture loops
Eyes flicker, yet holding their steady gaze

A frantic struggle; minefields go off inside her
*Follow me darling, forever can be yours and mine*
Hypnotic dragons encircle her, breathing their silver fire
*Give in my darling, eternity desires you*
She is at last free, her reward has finally come
Death comes but life sway on
Eyes dance.

***Shuwei Fang  (14)***
***Prior Park College***

## THE TIGER

The tiger gets up and stretches while the sun goes down,
She goes out on to the plains where the antelope gather,
There they are her prey.
They are there alert while eating,
One wrong move and they will flee away,
Slowly and steadily she moves nearer,
Crouching low to the ground.
Then she *pounces* high into the air,
The antelope scatter.
She finds the weakest and picks on it.
One great leap and she's on top of it,
It falls to the ground in one great heap.
All the others have disappeared from sight,
All you can see is the tiger and its prey.

*Laura Eatwell (11)*
*Prior Park College*

## CHANGES

Autumn leaves are falling down,
Twirling softly to the ground.
All the colours fade away,
It's winter now, it's time to play.

Snowflakes appear across the land,
Try and catch them if you can.
Children run out to dance and sing,
Snowmen arise, come and see.

Animals go away to sleep,
They find some fruit and nuts to keep.
Hibernating under a tree,
No creatures around for us to see.

Winter is now no more
My snowmen have sunken into the floor
Spring is now bright and clear,
The birds are singing for us to hear.

*Natalie Mogg  (11)*
*Prior Park College*


## DIVORCE

Within this crushed family I saw no hope.
The shouting went on for what felt like months,
My mother's crying never ended,
My parents' eyes were full of lies,
The isolation I felt was unbearable.
I wanted to cry, but I knew I had to be strong,
I used to switch off my mind and just lie still.
The counsellor couldn't or wouldn't understand.
Through the darkness I saw no light.
I prayed for peace but it would never come.
This period of my life felt like eternity.
My family was nothing but broken pieces,
I wouldn't wish this pain on anyone
And I wouldn't repeat these feelings for anyone.

*Camilla Pitt  (14)*
*Prior Park College*

## THE KOSOVO CRISIS

K ids screaming and crying,
O ver the bombed hills they flee,
S houting stop to any truck or plane they see,
O utside the danger is not certain,
V andalising the streets and houses too,
O n top of the hill they say their goodbyes.

C hanging ready for their enforced pilgrimage,
R ed blood making streams,
I rritations start to build up,
S moke and flames fill the air,
I njured people flooding hospitals,
S elfish armies raid the cities.

*Victoria Andrews  (11)*
*Prior Park College*


## SECRETS OF THE EMPYREAN

A fullness extensive and strange
captures our minds at a young age
mystical unanswered questions
an illusion on a blank page

Perched on the sky
dwelling softly between time
gushing out above, below
absorbed in secrets like mine

Smooth, sensual, silent
floating swiftly like a swan
loved and cherished
until all life has gone.

*Lia Bellaccomo  (16)*
*Prior Park College*

## MONSTERS

Monsters have a unique laugh,
Personal, and to themselves,
It's a sort of password,
Their laughs are kept in jars,
On very high shelves.

They have big green eyes,
And three nostrils,
But the strangest thing,
Is that they have no tonsils.

They have evil minds,
And only one ambition,
To eat men, stretch men,
Or to just squish 'em.

A few monsters have three eyes,
A few monsters have a tail,
A few have one leg,
Some you can receive in the mail.

Everyone knows Dracula,
Frankenstein and King Kong,
Some people know Satan,
Not many know the Japanese Mr Wong!

My perfect monster would be old,
With lots of hair and two feet,
He would know lots of magic,
And his name would be Pete.

*Graham Paterson (12)*
*Prior Park College*

## THE TWENTIETH CENTURY

Victoria dies, an Empire mourns, Bleriot flies to Dover alone.
Einstein's Theory makes scientists wonder, San Francisco nearly
quakes asunder.

Henry Ford builds his Model T, a Noble Prize for Madame Curie.
The Titanic sinks to a sad, icy doom, the Great War spreads its
murderous gloom.

Chaplin's little tramp gives joy to millions, Alexander Fleming
discovers penicillin.
John Logie Baird invents TV, Wall Street crashes into bankruptcy.

American wheat fields turn to dust, Jarrow marchers look for work.
Edward abdicates his throne, Garbo wants to be alone.
Nazis paraded their swastika signs, Poland invaded, no peace
in our time.

German blitzkrieg, French quickly fall, Dunkirk retreat, British backs to
the wall
Pearl Harbour attacked, America betrayed, D-Day starts the
Great Crusade.
Hitler dies, besieged in a bunker, Japanese skies explode in
atomic thunder.

War in Korea, Hungary suppressed, Edmund Hillary conquers
Mount Everest.
Castro seizes power in Havana, no home in Tibet for the Dalai Lama.

Kennedy dies by a gunman's hand, thousands perish in Vietnam.
Martin Luther King has a dream to share, Berlin is split by a
wall of despair.
Giant steps are taken by a man on the moon and the Earth revolves to a
Beatles' tune.

Egypt and Israel begin their search for peace, in a war-torn, ravaged
Middle East.
The Shah deserts his Peacock Throne, Ayatollah Khomeini rules
Iran alone.
Peace at last in Vietnam, Russian troops invade Afghanistan.
Falklands War, a Prime Minister rejoices, young men die because of
other people's choices.
African famine, Live Aid pays the bill, food for the starving, medicine
for the ill.
Chinese freedom destroyed and laid bare, crushed under tanks in
Tiananmen Square.

Nelson Mandela is free at last, to lead South Africa from its
apartheid past.
Saddam Hussein invades Kuwait, Serbia is bathed in ethnic hate.
Diana dies in a speeding car, Dunblane will forever bear a
madman's scar.

This century ends, the millennium too, the human race must start anew.
Love and trust can conquer all, evil and tyrants will surely fall.

*Holly Alston  (14)*
*Prior Park College*


## CHEETAH

It stalked around the water hole,
Getting ready to strike,
But the prey has seen her,
The chase is on.

She chased it through the moor and brush
But lost it all at waterfall,
She looked for a place to hide,
And the predator seized the moment and . . .

*Matt Cordon  (12)*
*Prior Park College*

## QUEEN OF THE HEAVENS

As another dark day begins the Queen of the Heavens looks down on
her children.
She blazes and stretches her fiery arms and all of her glory sparkles.
She is still, never stirred and has no friends.
She can only rely on her closest children Mercury, Venus, Mars
and Earth.
She protects them and holds them closely with a belt of stone.
They cannot escape her.
One of her daughters Saturn wears rings around herself from her
past husbands.
As time goes by her children chase her in circles never to give up
the fun and games.
She rises once more above her pride and glory, she shines her glittering,
light upon it.
She can burn anything that goes near her she has a licence to kill.
Don't go near the Queen Of The Heavens she is ready to pounce.

*Rebecca Clarke  (11)*
*Prior Park College*


## MONSTERS

Creeping, crawling the scary monsters are back,
The disgusting, slimy, scaly, creatures are on the run again.
They crawl and slither around the place.
If you dare go down to the monster world you have a horrible surprise,
There are all sorts of horrible creatures there,
There's the ugly great brute of Birmingham, who if you look at
him you die.
There is also the smelliest smute of Southampton, who if you smelt
you would be sure to die.
So there you have it the creeping, crawling, smelly, slimy,
scary monsters.

*Anna Greene  (11)*
*Prior Park College*

# LONELY MONSTER

When a monster comes out to play,
All the children run away.
Just because of the fact
That his fangs drip with blood,
That his claws were so long and sharp,
That his stomach once and always is craving for meat.
Just because of that.

He plays chase,
All on his own.
Chasing but his tail.
When he plays hide and seek,
He runs and hides
But no one seeks.

The bell rings,
Children pair off.
They walk in,
But Monster stands still,
Wind blowing his matted hair.
All are afraid,
All but he,

He is alone . . .

*aaaawooo . . .*

**Giverny Tattersfield**
**Prior Park College**

# LAST GOODBYE

The untouched soul lay,
Peaceful,
Undisturbed,
Long ago I knew him,
Happy in his play,
Forgetting his troubles,
His memory is always there:
Piercing blue eyes like crystals,
The never-ending smile.

Underneath I could feel the pain,
The anguish.
Some days I sensed a struggle within,
One more petal would fall,
Until his final day came,
When he would rest in peace.
I will never forget,
Can never forget,
That final smile,
The last goodbye.

*Caroline Jordan  (15)*
*Prior Park College*


# MY DAY

Today is an ordinary day,
but tomorrow who knows?
Maybe I'll become a millionaire
or maybe I will not.
But from day to day I'll
give a smile
and try not to be miserable.

*Fredderick Nandi  (14)*
*Prior Park College*

# THE BEACH

The sun comes up and all is calm,
The gleaming sea is rolling over the smooth golden sand.
The pure white gulls are calling with their soft voice,
And the rough cliffs making familiar face amidst the aqua blue sky.

Then swiftly the families come running in,
Children squabbling, adults shrieking,
Picnics, wind breaks, deck chairs all coming rushing out,
The lost child floods tears of loneliness and worry
He calls out a shout for his parents, but there is no reply.
The calls of the gulls have been drowned out by the
cluster of voices both excited and furious.

Then as quickly as the beach was full it was empty and
was left once more alone
The aqua blue sky was no more, the space was full of darkness,
The sand with large and tiny foot marks lay still.
The sun went down and all was calm
That was the way they liked it.

*Phoebe Hammill  (11)*
*Prior Park College*


# MONSTERS

M  onsters come in all shapes and sizes.

O  nly monsters are so slimy.

N  o monsters are at all friendly.

S  limy green saliva drooling out.

T  heir eyes gleaming like a fire.

E  very monster has its own roar.

R  unning after people, then ripping them apart.

S  o monsters are definitely revolting after all.

*Joanna Robinson  (11)*
*Prior Park College*

## IN AND OUT OF LOVE

No more time,
just the echoes of a
pledge made in the morning light,
so strong that no words were needed
to say it.

We both felt the wind blow through
our souls, as golden light slammed into the world,
kindling fires and setting our hearts aglow.

I felt the pangs of betrayal.
I'm afraid of the future.
My world is in a mess.
In my mind there is no time.
Lost, on a moonlit beach
in the firelight of a million stars,
I made a pledge, a new promise to myself.
No more pain.
No more broken hearts.
A new kind of life,
lived in the burnt-out shell
of my tortured soul.
No more crazy longings.
No more burning passions.
No more moments when she and I
are the only people in the world.
A new kind of life.
No more love.

*Laurent Rathborn  (14)*
*Prior Park College*

## MONSTERS

I was walking, I was alone,
It was what seemed
Like a normal night,
Until . . .

There was a scream,
There was a moan,
There was a gurgling of foam,
And from the darkness
Came . . .

A creature all slimy,
A thing that was climbing,
Up a building next to a tree,
I risked a glance,
Became in a trance
For there was . . .
A pair of eyes glaring at me!
Then . . .

There was a movement,
There was a fumble,
There was a distant rumble,
And down came the monster on me!
I lashed out in fury!
It's not the end of the story,
But . . .

It then took a swipe,
I ducked the bite,
But the monster followed me!
*Ahhh!*

*Megan Humphreys (11)*
*Prior Park College*

# A GOOD FRIEND

A good friend:
treats you equally,
makes you laugh,
someone you feel you can talk to,
someone who will make you look and feel great,
supportive,
will pick you up when you are down,
does not dominate the other,
does not force one to do something one does not want to do,
understanding,
sharing of possessions, secrets and friends,
serious when needed to be,
kind,
fun,
trustworthy,
does not leave one out, neglecting one,
willing to forgive
and to be reliable.

Many more you may think of,
but these are the qualities
most precious to me
in being a good friend!

*Nicola Pynegar  (14)*
*Prior Park College*

## THE SOLITARY SPIDER

A solitary spider
In autumn there are few
But some resist the onset
Suspensions hung with dew

I watch you scale my window
Thrown by gales of breeze
Yet you climb with precision
Motion judged with ease

You settle in a corner
Waiting for your chance
Vibration is detected
Across your lines you dance

A sleepy fly is tethered
Caught in layers of lace
But hopeless desperation
Is snuffed in your embrace

A clinical assassin
Inflicting only pain
Your despatch wrapped in silver
Is strung up in the rain.

*Daniel Richards  (17)*
*Prior Park College*

## REFUGEES

I see these people on the streets
I see these people on the buses
I see these people in my head
I saw these people screaming

I see their children's tired faces
Desperation - their only word
I see how people shun their being
People who have felt the same

A tear falls from my eye
I do not want to see their sadness
What is the price of human life?
Why do I feel this hurt inside?

I see the darkness in my soul
The guilt that haunts me has a name
I see my children crying for me
I cannot help but feel their pain

I see these people as myself
I see these people in the mirror
I see these people day-by-day
Now they show me who I am

They show me who I have to be
There is nothing left for me to tender
You and I are without love
A burnt out flame emitting no heat

I see these people
I feel their pain
They show my hurt inside
*They show me who I want to be.*

**Tom Fitzcharles (16)**
**Prior Park College**

# THE LONELY SILENCE

All my life I have stood here,
Looking down on the world,
From this lonely hill that is my home.
Haunted by the silence,
That has become my only friend,
The only sound I'll ever know . . .
Time is lost in years of sorrow,
Loneliness and tears.
All life has gone,
Leaving only melancholy stillness,
And me.
As alone I stand forever more,
All life is drained away.
The world below is fading,
Lost in a hazy mist,
Enveloping me
And then everything has gone.
The sun is blackened,
The sky grey,
All colours disappear
And as I feel the hands of death,
Reaching out to grasp me,
So icy-cold my heart becomes,
All pain is dulled,
And disappears into darkness.

*Samantha Lodge  (14)*
*Prior Park College*

## TEMPEST

The clouds are groaning overhead,
The water ripples with each chilling gust.
Boats in the harbour so pleasantly placed,
Start to sway, with the oncoming breeze.

As the storm approaches,
The streets of the nearby village are deserted,
But for a few seagulls picking at fallen crumbs.
Now, splats of rain begin their siege,
Shrouding the cloud-shadowed floor.

The mass of the waves increases,
Mauling the harbour walls,
Attempting to encompass them.
With the winds blustering into gales.

Now the storm is at its peak,
The waves disembowelling the smaller vessels
Whole trees are croaking,
Under the force of this almighty rage
The destruction is total, as the storm moves on.

The waves have proven devastating,
Seaweed flung to the roofs of houses,
The rain has flooded the hulls of boats
Villagers emerge to survey the scene.

*Charlie Elias  (14)*
*Prior Park College*

# A Strange Meeting

There he was,
A strange little creature,
So small and different.
He lay there totally silent.
All wrapped up in white cloth.
Just staring at me with his big eyes.
And gazing around at the white walls.
Taking in the whole atmosphere with one glance.
Then with his hand-like features.
He lunged towards me,
Like a lion at his prey.
Then a smile grew on his face
And his eyes filled up with joy.

I held him in my arms,
Then rocked him from side to side
And then he made a noise,
It was strange and made no sense.
Then his eyes seemed to get heavy
And his head fell back on my hand.
Then his eyes shut tightly,
And I stood there for a minute.
Staring, staring at my little brother.

*Rebecca Medlock  (13)*
*Prior Park College*

# TRENCH

*Boom!* Mud and blood thrown everywhere,
He joined because he was told it was the right thing
That it would be easy, over by Christmas.
All round him friends and compatriots were falling.
Many said Hague had a master plan,
He hadn't seen any evidence of it.

He had finally realised the futility of war
Thousands of men dying for a few metres of land.
In his boredom he would write,
Yet his hand shook so much that even to him it was illegible.
How much longer could this war go on?
One month, six months, a year? Anyone's guess!

New ladders were delivered with tons of explosive,
Puzzling everyone. We never got anything without begging,
Yet here they were!
Orders were given to dig a tunnel
Underneath the Jerries, and to place explosives in it.
Then came the order to prepare for the 'final push'.

Many were excited at the opportunity to let Jerry have some,
Others were petrified.
As they lined up at the parapet,
Many wondered what they would see.
He knew what.
Very little!

The guns went silent. Suddenly the sharp squeal of whistles.
The adrenaline kicked in, the typical fight or flight,
Those that fled would be shot in the morning,
Those that didn't were shot there and then.

*Andrew Bailey (15)*
*Prior Park College*

# MISSING

The cavernous hole remains,
His vibrant presence once enlightened all our lives.
Missing, they say:
Such a small word to describe the desperate fear and desolation.
Where is he?
What has happened?
Will he call?
Will he ever walk back through that door, smiling?

We hope,
We pray.
We are engulfed with a longing which is indefinable.
Missing, they say.
What does that really mean?
What will happen now?
We will wait,
We will wonder.
How long can we suppress the hysteria that boils from within?
It burns at the heart of our very being.

Sleepless nights followed by tortuous days,
Searching,
Searching.
Inching through the bleak hours of absent despair.
Then hope is blown apart,
Fragmenting our minds.
He is no longer missing,
he is never coming back.
It's over,
It's over.

*Sarah Jenkins (15)*
*Prior Park College*

# SISTER

They stand around her blurred
Their speech muffled.
Someone reaches out to her,
Spouting meaningless words.
They are trying to be sensitive
To understand how she feels,
But they can't they don't know.

How can someone say they've been there?
When they haven't, that they understand
When they don't.

How can someone sit, and comfort her
With lies?
There's nothing they can do
So why don't they just say so
And leave her heart to break in two.

*Charlotte F Davis*
*Prior Park College*

# THE HOWLING IN THE SKY

The clouds drifted over the sky
Around the winter trees.
Time to see what is really going on up there.
Autumn is a pretty time of the year.
Above the trees in the sky I think there are wolves up there;
I'm shivering with fear.
The ice trickles to the ground from my eyes.

The grass whips around my legs
So I want to scratch them.
That's better, I love doing that, that's what I call fun.
There are howls from the forest once again.
I think to myself why are they howling?
Are they hungry, maybe?
I look to the strange creature as sweat drips down my head.

*Robert Watkins (11)*
*Prior Park College*

## THE PARADE

'Left, right, left, right, left, right, left!
Squad, halt!'
Precision in its entirety.
Dress - identical,
Stance - identical,
Glares - identical.

All is motionless,
Not a voice to be heard.
The wind whistles through their hair,
Their sleeves flapping in desperation,
Like a bird in a cage.

'Right Turn!'
The squad moves as one uniform body,
Like a ballerina - so meticulous,
Like an orchestra - so synchronised,
Like a surgeon - so scrupulous.
'Left, right, left, right, left, right, left!'

*Emilia Lascelles (15)*
*Prior Park College*

## THE BULL

I am The Bull.
I am overlord of all that I survey.
I can see things that others cannot see,
Feel things that others cannot feel.
Worship me.
I can sense your innermost fears,
Your innermost passions.
I am your greatest fear,
Your worst nightmare,
Your most passionate dream.
All must cower before me,
And those who dare challenge me must fall back,
Even as the sea must fall back as the moon repels him.
I am your god.
Red,
Flushed with the blood of all those that kneel before me,
Splattered with that of all those who dared stand in my way.
Immortal and terrifying.
I am The Bull.

*Siobhan Thompson  (15)*
*Prior Park College*


## HUMANITY'S CRY

Out of the bemused jungle he steps,
blood-stained clothes grip his wounded skin,
the gun heavy under the concept of sin,
fighting at twelve for no concrete cause,
trying to cry but no time for to pause.

Time stands still and there he appears again,
now on the other side of the world.
Emotions withheld from the lives he controls,
at every swipe of the machete his authority retained.

Other continents feel him there,
just like the tabloids which depict him,
yet now he has a gun in order to kill,
gunfire smothering humanity's shrill.

In Africa, Middle East and Vietnam,
the world has witnessed this youth.
A youth of destruction, a youth of hate,
the youth of the future unless we contemplate,
trying to solve humanity's crime, before it's too late.

*Charlie Hoyle  (15)*
*Prior Park College*


## ANTICIPATION

As I lie in my bed,
I can feel it coming.
Like a bat from hell
It screeches through the unsuspecting night.
Never pausing, never wavering,
Like a condemned bullet from a gun.
I am stranded,
As if I am on a lonely desert island.
I am alone; no one will even know
Whether or not it reaches me.
It is no use trying to hide,
It will find me,
No matter how hard I try
To escape its icy grip.
And once it has got me,
It will never let go,
And I will wish for my lost loneliness
And cry out for the end of my torment.

*Katherine Bailey  (13)*
*Prior Park College*

# BLACKNESS

My shoes crunch the old stones,
Stones of three hundred years of history.
It's as if I'm walking over bones,
For this place of warmth and love,
Is so dead.

A place once full of life,
People running, shouting, talking.
The church echoes every sound.
Now cobwebs cover this image,
With their silken deceit of covering the dead.

A room once full of children laughing,
Is a room full of broken desks,
And light urging to get through to the blackness,
Which lies within this room.
The blackness in my heart.

I close my eyes,
The image appears once more,
I can hear it clearly now,
Each laugh different.
Wrapped up in its own immense humour.

Then I'm opening them,
I'm here amidst dead ghosts.
Whitening, cooling around me.
I breathe in but the air's musty and cold.

The sun's milky texture,
Dies as it sets,
It takes me with it,
On its long warm journey,
For I don't want to be here anymore.

With the cold unforgiving air,
Its lack of sympathy,
Which surrounds me,
Its emptiness,
Dead at the bottom of my heart.

*Nathasha Goldsworth  (15)*
*Prior Park College*


## LIFE IS . . .

Life. Short.
Painfully begun, often painfully ended.
Ended slowly, ended quickly.
It's all the same.

Life. Fragile.
An embryo, a macho-man
Are equally vulnerable,
Like a delicate, intricate flower. Easily crushed.

Life. A trial
Or a tribulation.
Joy. Grief. Sorrow. Happiness.
Emotional fancy? Or the key note?

Life. A mirage.
Is it real? Is it tangible?
Is it a test? Are we failing?
But what do we know?

We're pawns in a game.
We know nothing.

*Richard Olney  (15)*
*Prior Park College*

# SPACE

Back to the dawn of time,
Where the world didn't exist,
All there is are clouds of mist
Then suddenly a bright light
And a big bang!
The universe has been born.

Shooting stars and whizzing planets,
Clouds of hot burning gas
Sweltering suns
Exploding nebulae,
Shining stars
Sucking black holes.

And bulging gas planets
Bustling life and aliens,
People in spacecrafts
Travelling to distant space stations.
Comets and asteroids zooming around
Flying into dusty clouds,

Suns are dying and going red
Lots of things are now dead,
The universe is getting smaller
The universe is getting hotter and brighter
Brighter, brighter, hotter, hotter
And then - *bang* the universe is *gone!*

*David Leach  (12)*
*Prior Park College*

# AUTUMN TIME!

Conkers fall to the ground,
Splitting open as they land.
Shining in their silky cases,
Falling into people's faces.

Leaves are blowing off the trees,
In the nippy autumn breeze.
Golden leaves which once were green,
Autumn colours to be seen.

Farmers collecting all the crop,
Cutting and reaping *chippety-chop.*
· Mowing the grass in the fields,
Up and down the bumpy hills.

Foggy mornings it's freezing cold,
Everything looks oh so old.
White frost on the rooftops,
And heavy mist in the copse.

No animals around anywhere,
Not foxes rabbits or even a mare.
Most have crawled into their holes,
Gone for the winter including the moles.

*Laura Barnes (11)*
*Prior Park College*

## SWEETS!

Millions of sweets,
Waiting to be scooped up in a bag,
Lying in a bed of sugar,
Or in a jam-packed jar like sardines,
Then, suddenly a giant shovel,
Capturing them like prisoners.
That's the end until the next customer!

Then there is the old mouldy sweets,
Sitting in a sticky jar, all dusty.
Year after year, getting older and older,
But the scariest part is the black hole.
All smelly and dark, with mouldy bits,
As steep as a cliff . . .
*The bin!*

Here comes the delivery man,
Month after month,
In long dirty overalls,
Struggling through the doorway,
Carrying a brand new jar,
All clean and shiny
Taking up the old space on the shelf.

That's the end of the mouldy sweets,
Until next month,
Until all the mould builds up again
Growing rapidly inside the jar,
As each customer walks by,
Not even fluttering an eyelid,
Simply sitting on a shelf . . .
Being ignored.

*Laura Snowise  (11)*
*Prior Park College*

## To Die Is To Be Born

When you're born your life begins,
A sweet fearless bundle of what is to come,
You're here now and life has started,
The future's in your hands; the world your pearly oyster.
Your innocence is your guardian angel,
And age your one protection,
But when you're old and young at heart, age, will be your
                                        one reflection.

The first day at school is drawing near and Mummy's getting sad,
But I think I'm going to like it there with paint and sand and pens.
What's to come is what scares me and what has passed does too,
Though when the nights are cold and damp I think of what's to be,
Of boys and girls and castles wide, of knights with chivalry.

Your children are all grown up now; they're scattered far and wide,
You're one of two who started out in marriage an age ago.
In this time, life has taught you, one sweet myth; you sought
                                        for time again,
Though now you're on your own once more, and years have
                                        passed you by,

That one sweet story goes like this,
That when you're born you die.

*Fionnoula Edwards  (14)*
*Prior Park College*

## GHOSTS!

The night is drawing in,
Mysteries and shadows are dancing,
I am a mystery, you would hate to meet me,
I whisper around the countryside,
I float around and deceive you,
By covering you with my murky hands.
I'm silent, thick and blurred.
My sinister ways make you choke.
I am like an animal waiting to pounce on its prey.
I haunt you day and night.
I don't always win because of the wind,
I silently drift away, though I'll be back.

*Lucy Whittington (11)*
*Prior Park College*

## GIRAFFES

I stand out from the rest,
Because of my big body.
It is quite fun being so tall, as it feels
Like I can see the whole wide world.
I suppose not many people think of me,
As their favourite animal.
Maybe they are scared of us, because of our height.
But really we are very kind natured.
No one will come near us,
As they don't know what we will do.
But we don't mind, as we are quite happy.
So now think of us as beautiful, harmless creatures.

*Hannah Smith (12)*
*Prior Park College*

# TABLE

The table is by the window,
The window is under the stairs.
And here she sits day after day,
Staring out at the beautiful bay.

I'd look on in wonder,
How could she ignore me?
I'm left in a daze,
What can be there?

And then mother will come,
And stroke her hair,
Tell her not to worry,
But what is there?

I'm told not to stare,
As she sits on that chair.
Could it be that Alfie died,
Is that what makes her sit dry-eyed?

Can it be that that's caused the pain,
Is that what makes her call his name?

I know she'll never be the same.

***Ruth Mandeville  (14)***
***Prior Park College***

# FLORA

I walk out on the sharp
Green sponge.
Taking in the happy people.
They wear the hats,
To prove their beauty.
I kneel next to the smiling children,
Take my weapon.
Load up the barrel, with my power.
Their eyes look worried,
Who shall I choose for my display?
The pink one, the red one?
Cut, they fall, their sap draining.
Death for my pleasure,
I kill to let others smile.

*Fiona Brooks  (13)*
*Prior Park College*


# DARKNESS

It creeps into your room from every angle.
Your room becomes darker.
Now the light is gone you feel cold.
The gentle light of the moon filters through your curtains.
All is as still as can be and you hear the distant cries of a wolf.
It chills you sending a shiver down your spine.
Your ears become sensitive to every sound.
You feel as though you could hear the woodlice in the walls.

There is a cool eeriness in the room as if someone was watching you.
You hear creaks in the floorboards outside your room.
Grabbing the covers tight up against your neck, you don't dare move.
The handle begins to turn; you turn your head away.
The door opens and the light flows into the room.
I don't dare to look at who it is.
Lying there shivering I hope it is Mum.
The door closes and all is dark again.
Has it gone out or is it still in here?
All I know is that it's becoming colder and colder.
But I have a warm breeze blowing gently on the back of my neck.

*Andrew Papadopoullos  (14)*
*Prior Park College*


## QUEEN MAB

He loves me, he loves me not?
Love?
A musty tradition that haunts my soul.
As if someone is walking over my grave,
Possessing my mind influencing my thoughts.
Is it just a conspiracy to hide me from the truth
Disguised behind a pretty face?
Why am I imprisoned in a torture to hurt?
Temptation is overcome by curiosity.
Shall I blank dishonest advice?
Is it a warning for the future?
One day I will know.
One day Queen Mab will strike again.

*Isabelle Lawrence  (15)*
*Prior Park College*

## RESTING PLACE

Ahead of me a mountain lies,
A path is etched before my feet.
From foot to foot my body swings,
Along this endless track of time.

He peered through the swirling mist.
Beads of rain ran down the glass.
Far below streams score through hills.
He strained to find a landing place.

My legs grow tired, I stop to rest.
A crow swoops up and over the peak.
Yet another false horizon,
Where will this daunting mountain end?

The bombs had been dropped,
The damage done,
And now one goal remained,
To find his way back home.

I see the tangled wreck before me strewn,
Like a black and white image from a forgotten film,
A mark in time, a wormhole to the past.
What memories in that rusting metal lay?

His view was blind beyond the mist and fog.
Across the sea the fog was their mask,
Now over their land it was the evil of death.
The engine droned on into the night.

He did not see the hidden peak,
I did not see the hidden bones,
He could not escape his awful fate,
I could not picture such a death.

From past to present,
Two minds did meet.
He was at war,
I am at peace.

*Will Laslett  (14)*
*Prior Park College*


## MY GOAL

There is always one thing
I have wanted to see
To stand up tall and find beauty
I don't mean models, make-up and clothes
But happiness within instead of woes.
I ask myself what this beauty is:
Confidence, courage, love?
The ability to reach down into my soul
And feel good inside, yes that is my goal.

I know I can find it, just give me the strength.
I want to see the end it seems an eternal length.
For deep down inside there's hope and calm,
Beauty, peace, feelings, never any harm.
Give me the courage to battle on,
To finish once and for all it's been really long.
I know that by facing my fears I'll get there,
By finding my true self and crawling out of my lair.

*Nicola Darke  (15)*
*Prior Park College*

## THE DAY THE WORLD (AS WE KNEW IT) CAME TO AN END

As the hour dawned ever closer
A mixture or emotions were felt.
Some of which were happiness or fear;
That this technological-dependent world
Would finally come to an end

However when the hour did come,
Emotions could not have been felt
For within one swoop
The world seemed to die,
The people still breathed
But the world did not.

Everything stopped in its tracks.

Televisions stopped blaring, planes fell out of the sky,
Electricity stopped running and satellites crashed.
Yet a bigger trauma was of the human kind;
Their world as they knew it finally came to an end.

'What shall we do now?'
'There's no TV!';
'The light switch doesn't work!'
'I can't really see!'

These cries were heard throughout the world;
Yet now is a thing of the past.
For twenty years on
Mankind is worse than ever before
With less free will than ever before.

All independence has now been robbed,
We'll never get it back.
Self-sufficiency is a thing of the past
But learning to survive in changing times
Is a thing of the future.

*Finbarr Cosgrove  (14)*
*Prior Park College*

## LIFE IN THE TRENCHES

The icy tentacle of death creeps up on you,
Pulling you down to where there's no return,
Like an octopus, able to steal many at a time.

The bullets are like a wind that breezes over,
Almost silently to our deafened ears,
Lying here in the mud all you can feel is fear.

There is an overpowering smell of human flesh,
Everywhere you look there are your friends,
They seem to be staring at you even though their eyes are closed.

Your toes, fingers, face and feet are all frozen,
There are cuts and bruises all over your body,
Everywhere around there are people with fatal wounds.

Surrounded by bodies you cannot think,
You have killed men like yourself with the weapon in your hand
A shell explodes nearby, you are terrified.

*Bertie van der Beek  (14)*
*Prior Park College*

## A NEW LIFE

While sitting there,
Us watching him,
He seems to come alive,
This little bundle in his arms,
The start of a brand new life.
Could it have been three years ago,
That he felt so much pain,
And then just recently,
Months ago,
He felt it all again.
This little boy, just five days old,
My grandpa almost eighty,
The sparkle in his light blue eyes,
That has returned of lately.
He's thinking things,
I'm not sure what,
But I could hazard a guess,
That now he is much happier,
In fact he's at his best.
Also just how lucky he is,
To see his great-grandchild,
To see what he has created,
And that has made him smile.
But through this smile,
I can see,
Another thought in there,
A thought, that while he sees this boy,
He wishes my gran was here.

*Sophie O'Donovan  (15)*
*Prior Park College*

## CRY, THE TORTURED PEOPLE

They play so freely in the hazy sun,
And yet don't know of all the pain to come.
Their innocent young minds do not yet know
How could this happen be he friend or foe?
The torture of our people in this place,
The crime against religion and our race!
When did our people do such cruel things?
Since when did these foul demons rule our kings?
Cry out my faithful people let them see,
How strong we are and they could never be,
Fill full your hearts with God's undying love
And send to him your prayers on wings of doves,
So play my children, play in all your ways
I pray you never see these hell-filled days.

*Kate Roberts  (16)*
*St Mary Redcliffe & Temple School, Bristol*


## TIME

Time is plenty but yet slipping away,
Time is long when things stand in your way.
Time is short when there is much to do,
Time is little when it matters to you.

Time brings age leading to death,
Time brings sadness when people rest.
Time brings beginning when a baby is born,
Time brings happiness in love that is sworn.

Time is long
Time is never-ending
Time will keep our lives commencing.

*Charlotte Rudd  (12)*
*The Royal High School*

## THE DANCE OF THE DEAD

The empty house stood,
Ripped by shards of lightning,
Dead trees with clawing fingers,
Snatching, catching.

This is the scene,
And this is the Dance of the Dead.

The heavy doors creaked,
A voice not heard for years,
Admitting silent guests,
To its dark and derelict bowels.

This is the house,
And this is the Dance of the Dead.

They danced with deathly partners,
Clapped to silent music,
Voicelessly singing their chants.
In velvet and lace.

These are the people,
And this is the Dance of the Dead.

*Charlotte Kingston  (13)*
*The Royal High School*

## THE SENSES OF WAR

*I can see* the bodies on the ground,
Guns firing and shells exploding everywhere,
Mud covering everyone,
The enemy on the other side just like you.

*I can hear* the men shouting, screaming and groaning,
As they lie in no-man's land, dying,
Shells exploding very fast,
With a huge bang lighting the smoky sky.

*I can smell* the gunpowder and
The dirty air, smoke and ash
From the shells
The rotting dead bodies and the smell of fear.

*I can feel* the mud all around me
The loaded gun under my arm
My feet wet, muddy and sore
Wet clothes clinging to my body.

*I can taste* the rotten air in my mouth,
The same bully beef, plum and apple jam,
Over and over again, my mouth dry,
Thirsty for a beer.

*Helen McDill  (12)*
*The Royal High School*

## WORDS OF TOMORROW

Standing alone,
I hear in the silence
The echoing past.

Speeches of courage,
Fearful whispers.
A ranging spectrum of words.

Not one alike.
Each one, when spoken, shaped by language
As individual as the person who speaks them.

Mere marks on paper.
A jumble of these marks, looking so meaningless
Yet harnessing such power.

So often occurring
Many do not influence us
But carefully chosen, can change.

Power to change the past,
To change today,
And only they can touch the future.

Enveloped in a shroud of mystery
Tomorrow will be shaped by the words of the past.
We are living in tomorrow.

For yesterday, today was tomorrow.
So while we never reach the tomorrow of today
We are in the tomorrow of yesterday.

And we have conditioned today through words.
The power of words often goes unseen.
Yet without them, yesterday would not have occurred.
Today would be a void.
And there would never be tomorrow.

*Abigail Davis  (13)*
*The Royal High School*


## WHAT IS GOD?

Is God what men say He is?
Is He a woman?
Is He a dog?
Is He a flea?
Is He a river or a sea
Or is He just a figment of men's imaginations?

Where is God?
Is He in heaven?
Is He in the clouds?
Is He in the centre of the Earth
Or of the universe?
Is He in our food?

Who is God?
Is He a ghost?
A man with ultimate knowledge:
A baby?
A toad?
A thing man made up to comfort him?

Or is He real?

*Jennifer Hawke  (12)*
*The Royal High School*

## THE PEBBLE

One day, as I walked along the beach
I saw a glittering star amongst the sand
I picked it up and it shone in my hand
Like silver and even gold.

I couldn't bare to part with it,
So I held it in my hand all the way home
It flashed in the evening sun and it
Caught my eye and I was dazzled.

As soon as I got home, I put it in some water,
And placed it in pride of place
On my bedside table.
It shimmered through the water,
Like a jewel of the sea.
When I went to bed and the light had gone out
I looked at it in the darkness and it still shone at me.

It shone like a lighthouse over the sea of darkness
It comforted me and the sight lulled me to sleep.
The next morning, I looked for my shining star
But all I saw was a dull pebble in some water.

It was a dirty, white stone
And as it lay in the bottom of the glass
I wondered what I ever saw in it.

*Claire Rawlinson  (13)*
*The Royal High School*

# MY LITTLE SISTER

Waking up at midnight,
Knocking on your bedroom door,
Flicking food over the table,
Then painting the kitchen floor.

Embarrassing the family,
Walking naked down the street,
Messing up the living room,
Making mud pies out of peat.

Spilling cocoa on my homework,
Hiding all my clothes,
Squeezing out the toothpaste,
Then spreading it on Mum's rose.

Tearing my favourite poster,
Hogging the computer games,
Bouncing on the sofa,
Then squealing at her name.

Writing rude words on the wall,
Breaking my nicest toy,
Lagging behind on the way to school,
And trying to kiss my friend Roy.

Sister, sister try and be nice.
Just for once in your whole little life!

*Jenny van Griethuysen (13)*
*The Royal High School*

## THE MAN

He is always there
Sitting on the same street
Outside the same shop
Wearing the same clothes

He can't afford a house of his own
Even clothes and sometimes food
The only income he ever gets is selling the Big Issue

Wondering where he will sleep the next night
Or where he can scavenge food
How he will keep warm in the middle of the night
He has a dog to think of too

People are put off by his tattered old clothes
His long and matted beard
And rarely speak to him
But don't judge too soon he could be the nicest person you know

When you walk past he raises his cold scrawny hands
To ask for food or money
It wouldn't break the bank to give him a pound or two
It could buy him food for the next two days
But with it would be gone in a second

So it makes you think
You are well off
Unlike the man who is always there
In any season come rain, sleet or shine.

*Jessica Eagan  (12)*
*The Royal High School*

## DEATH BY CHOCOLATE

Sweet and dark and dangerous
How can I resist?
How can I ignore it?
I know I must persist

It's calling me, it's haunting me
I cannot go to sleep
I'm tossing and I'm turning
I tremble and I weep

I'm opening the cupboard
But I mustn't, no I won't!
It doesn't really matter if I eat it or I don't

It's lying there all innocent as if I have a choice
As if I can ignore the calling
Of its honeyed voice

I take a bite
Oh no too late
My fate now has a seal

And all the dreadful things I've heard
Have now become too real

I fly up the stairs with a hop, a skip, a bounce
I'm on the scales
Oh no it's true
I have put on an ounce.

*Heloise Hotson  (13)*
*The Royal High School*

## WHEN I AM OLDER . . .

When I am older
I will do the wonderful
and unbelievable
I will do the things that
everyone says is impossible
such as
To soar through the air
Like a bird, but without
a motor.
To vanish in a flash
and appear somewhere else
to travel back in time
to the age of the dinosaurs
to transform into water.
To find a cure for all diseases
when I am older I will do the
unthought, that people
only dream of doing
I shall land on new planets
talk to animals
I shall prevent hurricanes
save the world from pollution
when I am older.

*Holly Badenoch  (12)*
*The Royal High School*

## TEARS FOR THE WORLD

That night I found my child
Tearing at her bruised skin
Trying to change it.

As she was, she had been beaten
For being her
For the colour of her skin.

For her feet and hands
For her smiling face
Smiling no longer.

I cried for the world
And for the cruelty we are wont to inflict
And for the children.

And I hoped that it would change
Although deep in my heart
I knew there would always be hate.

And I loved
I loved those who had broken my child
Because I knew that without love
They would never change.

I kissed my child
I told her that to cry would not help
I told her to love, but to fight for what she believed
She listened
She slept. And she never woke again.

*Rachel Skevington Britton  (12)*
*The Royal High School*

## THE ANSWERERS, A PARODY ON THE 'LISTENERS'

'Is there anybody there?' said the cowboy
Knocking on the double swing doors
While his Quarter Horse in the silence
Ate some scrub from the desert's sandy floor
And a vulture flew out of the swing door
Above the cowboy's head
And he rapped on the door a second time
'Ain't there no one there' he said.
But no one came to greet the cowboy
No head from the dust fringed sill
Leaned over and looked into his snake eyes
Where he stood rock-hard and still
But only a host of bar men
That dwelt on the 'Lone Star' then
Stood sniggering in the quiet of the candlelight
To that voice from the world of outside
But eventually one gave it away
He couldn't help screaming 'Surprise!'
In fact they had a great party
'Neath the starred and dusty sky
After the surprise birthday
The cowboy galloped away
He said goodbye with a wave and his horse said 'Bye' with a neigh.

*Rhiannon LeParmentier (12)*
*The Royal High School*

## Nothing But A Tear

Nothing but a tear may be shed,
For loved ones in the land of dead,
Nothing but a tear in an eye.

Tears for friends,
For relatives,
For a lonely traveller on a dusty road.

Tears for happiness,
For sadness,
For a person that will never be seen again.

Tears for the starving,
For the hungry,
For the thin beggar calling out.

Tears for the sick,
For the ill
For the people in pain.

Tears for happiness
For loneliness
For nothing at all.

After all it's nothing but a tear.

*Victoria Donkin  (12)*
*The Royal High School*

## SPRING AND WINTER

Soft, smooth, falling snow,
The grass is wearing a new white furry coat
Studded with white, perky buttons,
Window frames share the glory,
Coated in soft, white flaky glitter
Snow is beautiful but nothing's worse
Than being caught in a blizzard,
At lunchtime on Christmas day.
Hungry, cold and tired,
Thinking of the wonderful roast
Turkey on the wooden table
And wishing yourself there.
Then, as if by magic,
A ray of light,
Shines through the clouds
And guides the poor child
Home to a warm house.
Then a great gust of heat
Soars through the door
All the children hurry to
The windows and gaze
Out to flowers and sun
A bright green coat
On the ground is left behind
Birds are singing in
The apple trees.

*Ashley Bhalla  (13)*
*The Royal High School*

## FUTURE VOICES

I'm rushing, I'm racing.
I'm stumbling and tripping.
The bracken is in my eyes.

The hounds are snapping, calling and yapping.
I hear their feet close by.

The hooves of the horses hit the ground,
Coming closer with every cry.

People are calling, shouting and laughing,
At least they seem to be enjoying the ride.

I'm tired, I'm hungry.
I just want to stop.
I know that my time is almost up.

The hounds are upon me, ripping and tearing.
The pain shoots unbearably up through my side.

But now I can't feel it.
My life slips away.
The noise is no more.

Tradition they call it exciting and fun.
When will they realise that fox hunting is wrong?

*Miranda Watkins  (13)*
*The Royal High School*

## CAR BOOT SALE

Our car drove through the field,
Past the plastic, waving barriers.
Bump, bump over the grass.
It was quiet.
A few people were setting up stalls.
Wide-boy traders bustled round the car.
I was scared of them,
Dad was tough.
'Stay away from there, don't touch that'

As the public arrived, the sale really began to start.
'How much is that?'
'What, five pounds? I'll give you four fifty'
The smell of candyfloss and hot-dogs filled the air.
People stepped over patches of mud.
Mothers chatted to old friends
Fathers looked for tools and old records
Babies screamed and giggled as they played
with a new toy.

Soon the general lull of noise was over.
The grass was trampled.
The bouncy castle was being deflated.
We packed up the stall and went bump,
bump back over the grass and home.

*Clare Wales  (14)*
*The Royal High School*

## MY OLD SCHOOL

Walking down the empty hall,
Memories flooding past me,
Empty lockers line the walls,
Is this really my old school?

Seeing my old form room,
Full of rusty old chairs.
Shadows cast a dark gloom,
The only light is from the moon.

Down the corridor is the gym
And the hall for assembly,
Used to be full of chatter, a din,
Now silent as ever, not even a hymn.

Outside in the cold night air,
The pitch is wet and muddy.
The grass that held the last summer fair,
Why did I come here just for a dare?

Running down the closed down hall,
I wondered why I had come.
Then I heard my mind call:
'Is this really your old school?'

*Amy Dunningham  (14)*
*The Royal High School*

# WEATHER OF THE WORLD

Sun, golden and radiant.
A beautiful, golden ball, floating in the baby-blue sky,
Surrounded by fluffy, white clouds,
Covering the Earth in a blanket of warmth and happiness,
Giving light to share amongst us -
A sunny day is a cheerful day.

Rain, glistening and shimmering.
Specks of water, tumbling from the oblivious sky,
Refreshing our bodies and minds,
Creating rippling puddles of murky water,
And feeding the Earth with life's precious fluid -
A rainy day is a freshened day.

Snow, cold and chilling.
White flakes of icy snow drifting from the vast, white clouds,
Rather like tiny winter fairies,
Fluttering and floating to the white ground below,
Bringing pleasure to adults and children alike -
A snowy day is a beautiful day.

Hail, hard and frozen.
Solid balls of cold, bitter ice,
Throwing themselves out of the frosty skies,
Raining hard and painfully on delicate heads below,
Bringing distress and suffering to the World -
A hailing day is a hated day.

Wind, draughty and rushing.
Moving air, gliding through the atmosphere,
Whistling down chimneys, resisting creatures walking,
Forcing umbrellas inside-out,
And bringing awkwardness to us -
A windy day is a demanding day.

*Rosie Harris  (12)*
*The Royal High School*

# THE POEM THAT I JUST COULD NOT WRITE!

I find it rather difficult to write,
A poem of twelve lines overnight,
I've struggled all the lesson and some more,
And now I'm lying on my bedroom floor,
I just can't seem to find a central theme,
Or talk about a deep or distant dream.

So I've got into a supernatural trance,
To give myself the most incredible chance,
The words will come flowing soon I know,
And then I'll have something done to show,
That I can do it if I really try,
And resist the urge just to sit down and cry.

*Holly Brown  (13)*
*The Royal High School*


# WHAT IS A PROMISE?

A promise is something that
should not be broken
A promise is something that
you should not tell
A promise is a secret
A promise is something that
you will do
A promise is trust
A promise is guarded
A promise is a waterfall that
comes out of your mouth
A promise is in your heart.

*Lizzy Epsley  (13)*
*The Royal High School*

## Paddington Lives

It's happened again
All they ever dreamed of
All they ever loved
Never to resurface
When the last train
Rushes along its last track
The red light flicks
But alas the brakes don't switch
It is hit
The flame has lit
And carriage H never to be seen again
There were shouts and screams and no more
As somebody tries the door
But we still mourn on this death day
For the Paddington souls lost
And as the day dies think of
The lives that this crash has cost.

*Caitlin Morgan  (12)*
*The Royal High School*


## Dreaming

Through the East door I go
Tripping over blobs of snow
How I wish I was in the warm
Away from the awful snowstorm

I'd sit with a warm cup of tea
Dreaming of summer by the sea
Lovely picnics on the cliff side
Watching the birds around me glide

Dreaming of being a famous actress
Will Marks & Spencer have that nice dress?
When will I meet my hero Brad Pitt?
Whoops have I washed Hannah's sports kit?

Dreaming will not help me at all
I've still got to go to the bookstall
Through the snow and over the hill
Please God don't give me a chill.

*Claire Emery  (13)*
*The Royal High School*


## THE LAND OF YOUR DREAMS

You step out of the plane,
A wall of hot air hits you,
The engines turn off and jilt you.

You step off the landing stage,
You're there, the place of your dreams fine and fair.

You see the small, slightly ramshackle airport,
A change to Gatwick, the size of twenty tennis courts.

The sea strikes you,
Turquoise blue, oh, and I wish you were here with me too.

The weeks pass by,
You know the time has come to fly
Wake up . . . wake up . . .
It's time for school,
But I think to myself 'I was just in the pool,'
I realise it was just a dream,
Oh, what a shame,
I want to be there again.

*Isabel Laister  (14)*
*The Royal High School*

## 00:00

This world has been taken over
With millennium fever
I myself am not a believer
The true meaning has been disguised
By expensive tacky merchandise

While we are celebrating
We should also be commemorating
Jesus Christ and all he did
He helped the poor when they were needy
Let's follow in his footsteps
And be less greedy

Do you really need a tacky toy?
Will it really bring you that much joy?
People are starving and have no homes
Yet we are building a Millennium Dome

This millennium
Don't disguise the true meaning
But join in the feeling
Of a happy new year!

*Charlotte Williams  (13)*
*The Royal High School*

## WINTER'S MORNING

Mist rose over the bleak hills
Frost hung from the tired, frozen grass
As the sun woke up into the cold, fresh sky
Winter's morning stood silent.

Snow glistened still and wet on the ground
White as white can be
Crystal snowflakes delicately floated through the air
Winter's morning stood silent.

Birds quietly twitter and snuggle up in their nests
Squirrels run up the numb tree trunks
Rabbits sleeping underground without a stir
Winter's morning stood silent.

Children drink hot cocoa in their beds
Some go out to play
Their breath hangs before them in a cloud of steam
Winter's morning stood silent.

Winter's morning stood silent.

*Jeanie Sondheimer (12)*
*The Royal High School*

# You're Not Going Out Looking Like That!

It's Friday night at eight o'clock and I'm all ready to go
My hair is done, my new clothes are on and the body spray has run low.

I walk down the carpeted stairs and tiptoe past the open lounge door.
I was nearly away through the kitchen,
when Mum heard a creak in the floor.

She got up and came to the kitchen,
but when she saw me she froze in her track.
Her jaw hit her feet and her heart skipped a beat
and she yelled, 'You're not going out looking like that.'

'Go up to your room you are grounded, no television or
chips for a week.'
'But please Mum,' I shout, 'I have to go out,
if I don't will look like a geek.'

Turning red with rage she started to scream,
'Don't argue or I'll punish you more.'
'Well fine,' I say as angrily as her and I walk out
slamming the door.

*Chantelle Williams  (13)*
*The Royal High School*

# LIFE IS . . .

Life is that pink frilly dress hanging in your wardrobe,
Life is a history essay,
Life is arguing with a sibling,
Life is a spider sitting on the end of my bed,
Life is your brother being top of the class,
Life is doing the housework,
Life is a football that our dog burst,
Life is one out of ten in maths,
Life is when your sister eats the last sweet,
Life is the school dinners,
Life is nothing to eat ever,
Life isn't fair!

*Laura Mathews  (12)*
*The Royal High School*


## COLOURS

What would we do without colours?
Everything would be nothing,
We wouldn't be able to choose anything,
We wouldn't be able to see anything,
We wouldn't be able to write anything,
We wouldn't be able to read anything,
We wouldn't be able to go to school,
We wouldn't be able to get an education,
All that we would see is nothing,
Without colours everything is nothing,
What would we do without colours?
We would be blind.

*Becky Pugsley  (12)*
*The Royal High School*

# VOICES OF THE FUTURE

Voices of yesterday echo through the hall,
Lonesome students scream and call,
Desperate to have their voices heard,
Hopelessly repeating every word.

Screams go unheard, shouts are ignored,
Voices go on calling, but no one applauds,
Time has gone by, the voices slowly die,
Whispers fade away, leaving only a faint sigh.

Future voices now come through,
New and fresh like the morning dew,
Now portrayed in a different way,
This is the start, a new dawn, a new day.

Calling, crying, shouting our views,
We need to be loud, to pass on the news,
We'll write it on paper and spread the word,
For we are the future and demand to be heard.

*Felicity Woodward (14)*
*The Royal High School*

# THE MATCH

Running up and down the pitch,
Channelling mud from many sides,
Panting with exhaustion,
As your hockey stick collides.

Wiping rainy glasses,
Droplets running down my nose,
Mass of heavy hair,
Goalie striking up a pose.

Charging up towards the ball,
Clutching on my hockey stick,
Tackling to win the round,
Tying to get a better grip.

Rushing in towards the goal,
Aiming with a flick,
But, at the last minute,
The goalie saves it with her stick.

*Katie Brockwell  (14)*
*The Royal High School*


## MY DOG AND THE FROG

One day I went a'walking,
Down to a park in Woking,
I took my dog to catch a frog,
At the end of this poem,
He's choking.

I was walking round the park,
And suddenly heard this bark,
It was my dog chasing a frog,
Right off the end of a drawbridge.

The pond was big, the pond was round,
My dog was sinking down to the ground,
He jumped out of the murky water,
Only to find out we were rolling with laughter.

My dog was cold, my dog was wet,
And he went running to the vet,
Nothing was wrong he was told,
But the next day he went down with a cold.

*Clare Nixon  (14)*
*The Royal High School*

# HER NAME IS CARCINOMA

Cancer is a bitter taste,
you can taste it at the back of your throat when you swallow,
a cloying smell
like stephanotis in a closed room.
She has a yellow face and dull eyes opened wide as if looking into an
open grave.
Her elbows; oversized pivots for wasted arms that hang.
When cancer swallows you can see the muscles pulsing with effort.
When cancer breathes you can hear the rasping noise as air is sucked in
desperately through her teeth.
Cancer talks a lot, but not to me.
I've been told quite kindly that 'it's the drugs'
but I hope that whoever it is that she is talking to, answers.
I try to interpret the strained noise,
I like to think I am the only one who understands her
but her words are so fragile that a breath obliterates them.
Cancer has her own language.
Her bones are shielded with only a thin layer of transparent skin
and I always stand away from her in case a sudden movement
pierces the cellophane.
Cancer has a swollen stomach;
a cruel illusion of life to the dying,
an unnatural growth that rips life and lives apart.
Cancer cannot eat and barely drinks
although I did think something sweet might tempt fancy
it seems that fancy is dying too.
She does at least know my name and I don't mind being
confused with figures of the past.
Cancer's room is dark and hot and airless like a tomb.
There is a small light in the corner of the room,
one night the light will be extinguished;
Cancer will have turned out the light and left the room.
Her breaths are slower now, reluctant.

Each pulse of the heart is chased by the tick of the clock,
soon the taunting tick will catch up with her internal clock
just too weak to keep up with the rhythm of life.
I think of her as the flickering light in the corner of the room,
as the moth beating its wings against the windowpane to get out,
I think; to explain away
the pathetic composition of flesh that stares at the ceiling all day,
that has lost all sense of modesty and pride
and lies dead, alive.
She never complains, though I'm not sure pain ever exists in her world.
She used to be considered brave, but is no longer brave.
She is nothing.
She has been taken over by a
vicious Virago, the most powerful female phenomenon
She brings a cold, crude, cruel death,
a cancerous death
And her name is Carcinoma.

*Clare Diacono (15)*
*St Mary's School, Calne*